Aircraft timbers are mainly formed from coniferous softwoods, principally Sitka spruce, which possesses the best compromise of the characteristics of weight, strength and availability. Because of the eminent suitability for aircraft building Sitka spruce is taken as the standard against which all other aircraft timbers are assessed. The stresses that occur in operational aircraft put a considerable strain on the timber employed and the properties of the wood itself are therefore more important than the properties of wood used in any other structural industry. Both the selection and inspection of suitable timber is therefore strictly controlled, for there may be many ingrown defects, some of which may not be immediately apparent, that could dangerously weaken its structural properties. Similarly, lack of care in seasoning and storage could adversely affect it. Fig. A indicates the position in the log from which lengths are taken to guarantee straight grain, minimal shrinkage and resistance to warp. Cut boards are seasoned in hot-air drying kilns, then stored under cover in raised and separated stacks to ensure free air movement. At all stages of its life timber may be subject to fungi, damp, or wood boring insects unless it is adequately protected. The weight of wooden aircraft is high in comparison to similar light alloy structures, and the lack of demand for wood to be used in mass production has caused many timber suppliers to stop handling sales of suitable wood, but despite these disadvantages the overall cost of a wooden aeroplane remains lower than that built of light alloys. This cheapness of construction coupled with the ease with which wood can be worked and shaped using typical workshop tools, will no doubt guarantee a promising position for wood in do-it-yourself aviation for the forseeable future.

A

B

4

5

6

7

8

Throughout aviation history, wood has been first choice for light and home-built aeroplanes due to its convenience and ease of use. Shown here are two examples of minimal aeroplanes, alike in purpose but separated by fifteen years of aerodynamic understanding.

Above: The Pensuti-Caproni triplane of 1921, one of several similar designs arising from an Italian Government-organised competition to find the smallest practical aeroplane. Wingspan was a mere 13 ft. (4 m.), powered by a 3-cylinder 35 h.p. Anzani.

Right: Henri Mignet's HM-18 of 1936, a cabin version of the celebrated but ill-fated Pou-de-Ciel, employing an improved undercarriage and wing-tilting operation, an elevator on the rear wing, and a 38 h.p. Menguin engine.

THE
WOODEN
WONDER

A SHORT HISTORY OF
THE WOODEN AEROPLANE

JAMES G. ROBINS

JOHN BARTHOLOMEW & SON LTD.
EDINBURGH

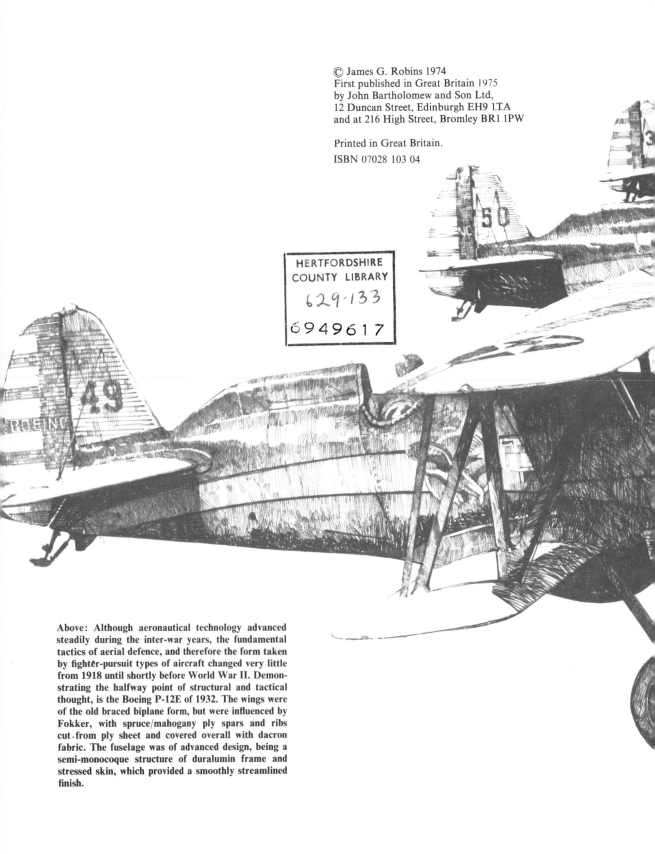

© James G. Robins 1974
First published in Great Britain 1975
by John Bartholomew and Son Ltd,
12 Duncan Street, Edinburgh EH9 1TA
and at 216 High Street, Bromley BR1 1PW

Printed in Great Britain.

ISBN 07028 103 04

Above: Although aeronautical technology advanced steadily during the inter-war years, the fundamental tactics of aerial defence, and therefore the form taken by fighter-pursuit types of aircraft changed very little from 1918 until shortly before World War II. Demonstrating the halfway point of structural and tactical thought, is the Boeing P-12E of 1932. The wings were of the old braced biplane form, but were influenced by Fokker, with spruce/mahogany ply spars and ribs cut from ply sheet and covered overall with dacron fabric. The fuselage was of advanced design, being a semi-monocoque structure of duralumin frame and stressed skin, which provided a smoothly streamlined finish.

CONTENTS

THE DREAM

The mastery of gliding was an important step towards the effective implementation of powered flight, living on as a major sporting interest. Both 'gliding' and 'soaring', in which the pilot flies a machine which is of necessity of low structural weight and the most efficient low resistance aerodynamic form, have constantly provided useful research for improving powered aircraft design. As well as being one of the few areas in which wood still plays a major part, it is also one in which plastic structures are being pioneered. Generally regarded as the first modern sailplane was Robert Kronfeld's 'Wien' (left) designed by Alexander Lippisch. With its narrow, high-aspect ratio wing and low-profile, low-friction monocoque fuselage it had significant aerodynamic superiority over its contemporaries which enabled it to set up numerous endurance and distance records in 1929. It was not unlike the Wandering Albatross, nature's master of soaring. The weakness of the bird's wing-motion muscles and legs signify its specialised development to this end.

INTRODUCTION

For many centuries man regarded flying creatures in awe, as the possessors of a capability well beyond his means. Thus flying passed into mythology—Gods and Great Spirits were given the power of flight to set them apart from the common man, this reverent attitude to flight clouding the reality and pure mechanics that could have made human flight possible.

Birds and bats were obvious examples to which man turned for the inspiration of flight, but the combined use of wings for both lift and propulsion was a constant source of confusion. Few designers seemed to realise that some birds flew quite satisfactorily without wild flapping of their wings, and that fixed wings might offer a more promising area of research into the marvel of flight.

Among the first to put flight on a scientific footing was that celebrated genius, Leonardo da Vinci. From his studies of bird wings and patterns of flight, he suggested that man could fly through the air by the use of flapping wings, steered by a tail-borne rudder, much in the manner of a bird's tail. Designs were prepared for flapping arrangements with the man in both prone and standing positions, and later for a helicopter; a name coined from the Greek by da Vinci himself. His design had a helical, or screw-shaped, aerofoil. His failure to make a success of his ideas was in part due to the inability of man to produce sufficient power by means of his own muscles, but more fundamentally it was a complete misunderstanding of the mechanics of bird-flight. Having failed, he no doubt dropped the subject and passed on to fresher pastures. It was unfortunate that although he had such diverse inspirations he never brought any of them to a satisfactory conclusion. Fixed wings with supplementary propulsion did not figure in his (recorded) estimations.

However, Leonardo had established an interest in serious experimentation in flapping wings (ornithopters) and man-powered aeroplanes, that inspired, misguidedly or otherwise, some of the World's greatest aviation pioneers. Among them were Cayley, Lilienthal, Hargreaves and Lippisch, and the interest continues to this day. Too often their efforts have provided great humour for the onlooker and aviation pundit, as almost without exception their efforts have been dramatically or embarrassingly unsuccessful. Perhaps there are still significant advances to be made, at least in the area of man-powered flight, even if it should only justify the efforts of a handful of inventive men, who to a cynical world are simply wasting their time.

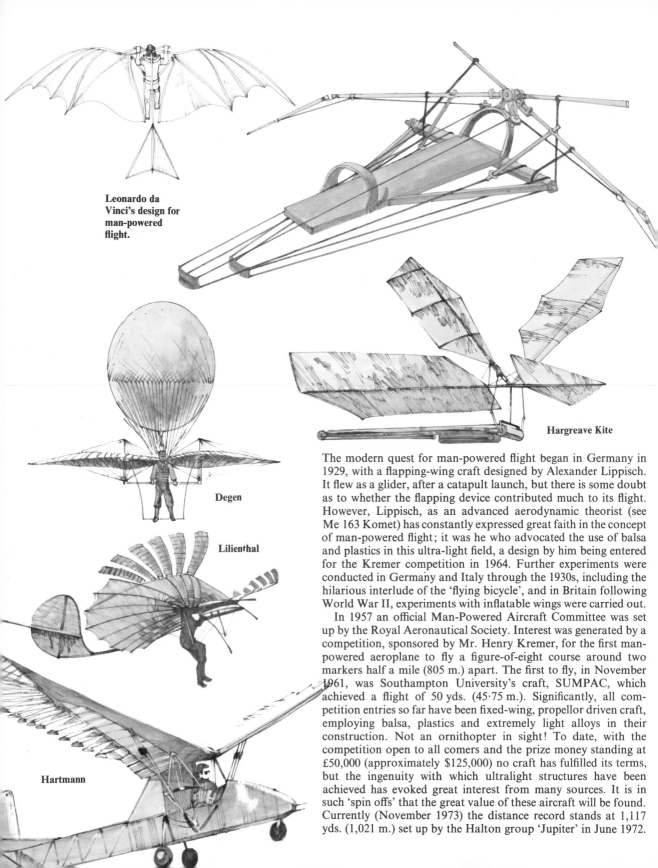

Leonardo da Vinci's design for man-powered flight.

Hargreave Kite

Degen

Lilienthal

Hartmann

The modern quest for man-powered flight began in Germany in 1929, with a flapping-wing craft designed by Alexander Lippisch. It flew as a glider, after a catapult launch, but there is some doubt as to whether the flapping device contributed much to its flight. However, Lippisch, as an advanced aerodynamic theorist (see Me 163 Komet) has constantly expressed great faith in the concept of man-powered flight; it was he who advocated the use of balsa and plastics in this ultra-light field, a design by him being entered for the Kremer competition in 1964. Further experiments were conducted in Germany and Italy through the 1930s, including the hilarious interlude of the 'flying bicycle', and in Britain following World War II, experiments with inflatable wings were carried out.

In 1957 an official Man-Powered Aircraft Committee was set up by the Royal Aeronautical Society. Interest was generated by a competition, sponsored by Mr. Henry Kremer, for the first man-powered aeroplane to fly a figure-of-eight course around two markers half a mile (805 m.) apart. The first to fly, in November 1961, was Southampton University's craft, SUMPAC, which achieved a flight of 50 yds. (45·75 m.). Significantly, all competition entries so far have been fixed-wing, propellor driven craft, employing balsa, plastics and extremely light alloys in their construction. Not an ornithopter in sight! To date, with the competition open to all comers and the prize money standing at £50,000 (approximately $125,000) no craft has fulfilled its terms, but the ingenuity with which ultralight structures have been achieved has evoked great interest from many sources. It is in such 'spin offs' that the great value of these aircraft will be found. Currently (November 1973) the distance record stands at 1,117 yds. (1,021 m.) set up by the Halton group 'Jupiter' in June 1972.

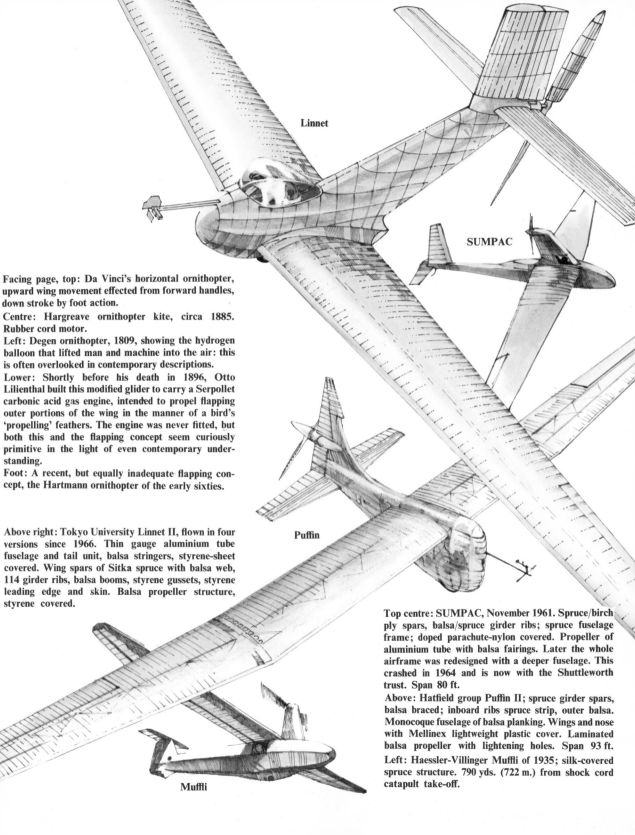

Linnet

SUMPAC

Puffin

Muffli

Facing page, top: Da Vinci's horizontal ornithopter, upward wing movement effected from forward handles, down stroke by foot action.

Centre: Hargreave ornithopter kite, circa 1885. Rubber cord motor.

Left: Degen ornithopter, 1809, showing the hydrogen balloon that lifted man and machine into the air: this is often overlooked in contemporary descriptions.

Lower: Shortly before his death in 1896, Otto Lilienthal built this modified glider to carry a Serpollet carbonic acid gas engine, intended to propel flapping outer portions of the wing in the manner of a bird's 'propelling' feathers. The engine was never fitted, but both this and the flapping concept seem curiously primitive in the light of even contemporary understanding.

Foot: A recent, but equally inadequate flapping concept, the Hartmann ornithopter of the early sixties.

Above right: Tokyo University Linnet II, flown in four versions since 1966. Thin gauge aluminium tube fuselage and tail unit, balsa stringers, styrene-sheet covered. Wing spars of Sitka spruce with balsa web, 114 girder ribs, balsa booms, styrene gussets, styrene leading edge and skin. Balsa propeller structure, styrene covered.

Top centre: SUMPAC, November 1961. Spruce/birch ply spars, balsa/spruce girder ribs; spruce fuselage frame; doped parachute-nylon covered. Propeller of aluminium tube with balsa fairings. Later the whole airframe was redesigned with a deeper fuselage. This crashed in 1964 and is now with the Shuttleworth trust. Span 80 ft.

Above: Hatfield group Puffin II; spruce girder spars, balsa braced; inboard ribs spruce strip, outer balsa. Monocoque fuselage of balsa planking. Wings and nose with Mellinex lightweight plastic cover. Laminated balsa propeller with lightening holes. Span 93 ft.

Left: Haessler-Villinger Muffli of 1935; silk-covered spruce structure. 790 yds. (722 m.) from shock cord catapult take-off.

Left: Pfalz D.III fuselage under construction, circa 1917. Fabric strips alternated with veneers for stiffening bulk. Casein cement. Man hours per airframe might have been twice those required for a Fokker welded steel unit.

Below: Mosquito half-fuselage shell under construction. The jig contained slots and recesses for bulkheads, stringers, stiffeners, etc. All openings were constructed integrally, to be cut out later. The narrowness of the fuselage made it necessary for many internal effects to be installed prior to joining the fuselage halves.

Foot: D.H. Albatross fuselage carapace being lifted from its jig, the sides of which collapsed inwards for clearance.

WHY WOOD?

INTRODUCTION

The structural forms of aeroplanes are not coincidental but are related to the properties of the constructional material, of current structural and aerodynamic theory, and of the economic, social and political implications of their use.

At no time has wood been the only material available to the plane-maker. Du Temple had advocated aluminium construction as early as 1857, and welded steel tube figured quite widely from the earliest days of practical flight, later supplanting wood for fuselage forms in the interest of mass production. Although possessing good weight/strength, flexular and impact-strength characteristics (sometimes superior to those of metal construction) the widespread continued use of wood in aviation was mainly due to its availability, economy and convenience of use. Similar reasons account for its continued popularity for amateur aircraft construction.

In general, as compared to metal construction, wooden aeroplanes were cheaper to build, with lower plant requirements, little specialised tooling and lower labour proficiency requirements; the flying structure was very stable, resistant in a broad range of stress factors, easy to maintain and repair. Monocoque shells, although heavier, were more simply and cheaply built, presenting a superior low-friction surface.

Top right: Pou-de-Ciel under construction, circa 1936. Wings awaiting fabric.

Right centre and foot: Wooden propeller preparation, generally of hardwoods like mahogany. Centre, carving a spinner boss; the blades are nearly finished. Foot, setting the laminations prior to shaping.

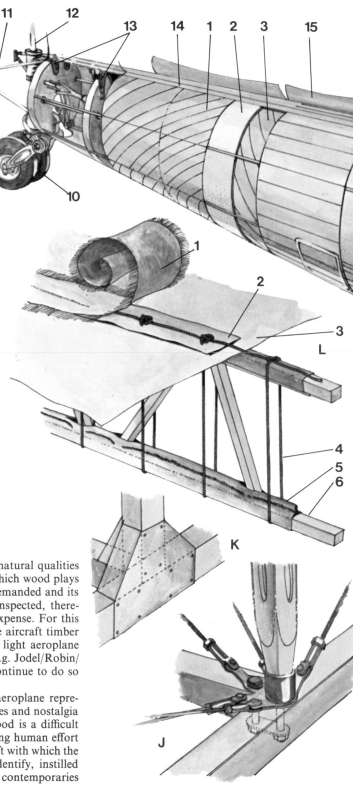

Right: Examples of early and late fuselage structures.

Upper: Farnborough S.E. 5a 1917; basic fuselage frame, typical wire-braced space frame. (1) Fuel tank brackets. (2) Steel joint plates. (3) Forward fuselage ply-covered, remainder cellulose-doped fabric. (4) Ply-stiffened bulkheads. (5) Ash engine bearers. (6) Steel tube wing spar extensions. (7) Steps. (8) Longerons and compression members of spruce. (9) Steel wire bracing. (10) Rudder post.

Lower: De Havilland Mosquito; ply/balsa/ply sandwich monocoque. Early bomber/P.R. type shown, fighters carried four ·303 in. Brownings in nose, four 20 mm. Hispano cannon in belly. One piece wing with fuel tanks in centre section torsion box. (1) 2 mm. outer birch ply skin. (2) 20 mm. balsa core. (3) 1·5 mm. inner birch ply skin. Rear fuselage veneers laid diagonally to counter torque. (4) Plexiglas nose. (5) Hatch/bomb-bay framing incorporated with skin, cut out later. (6) Laminated spruce, birch ply box spars. (7) Double upper wing skin. (8) Main fuel tank. (9) Bulkhead (7 in all). (10) Double-rim tailwheel. (11) Alloy tailplane spar supports. (12) Rudder post. (13) Fin attachment points. (14) Fuselage halves securing strip. (15) Madapolam (Madaplin) fabric overall. (16) Four 1 in. × 1 in. (25 mm.) spruce stringers between sandwich skins. (17) Spruce hatch frames. (18) Wing attachment points. (19) Observer's armoured position. (20) Pilot's seat.

Aircraft construction requires more from the natural qualities of timber than any other structural industry in which wood plays the major part. The highest quality material is demanded and its selection and preparation must be stringently inspected, therefore incurring a greater degree of wastage and expense. For this reason many suppliers have shied away from the aircraft timber trade. A few companies continue to supply the light aeroplane market with a mass-produced wooden aircraft (e.g. Jodel/Robin/CEA in France) and gliders, and are likely to continue to do so for some time to come.

Structural considerations aside, the wooden aeroplane represents an alternative to mass produced commodities and nostalgia for an old craft industry. By its very nature, wood is a difficult medium for automated mass-production, requiring human effort at every stage of construction; it is therefore a craft with which the plane-maker, aviator and onlooker alike can identify, instilled with a 'character' not possessed by its all-metal contemporaries and superiors.

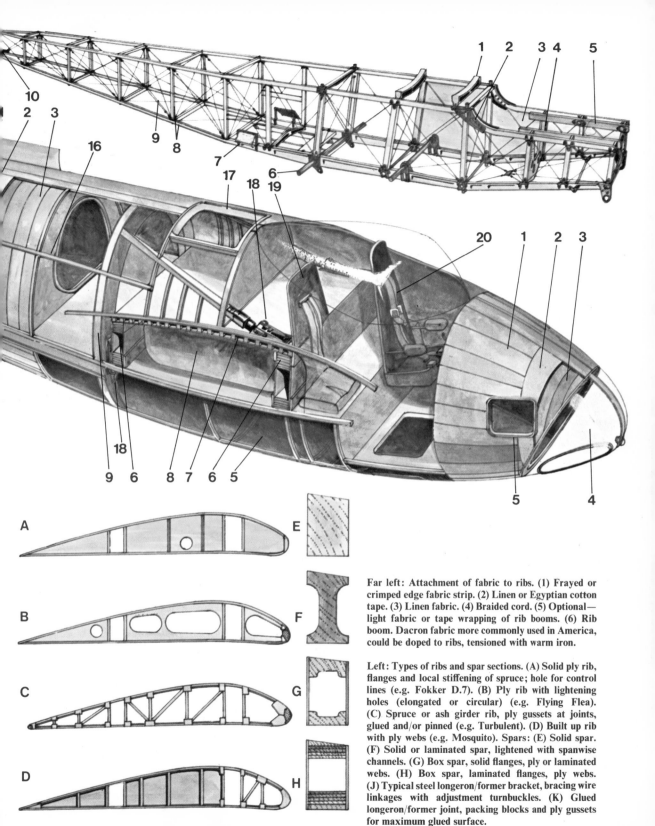

10
2 3
9 8
7
6
2 3
16
17 18
18 19
20 1 2 3
9 6 8 7 6 5
18
5 4

A

B

C

D

E

F

G

H

Far left: Attachment of fabric to ribs. (1) Frayed or crimped edge fabric strip. (2) Linen or Egyptian cotton tape. (3) Linen fabric. (4) Braided cord. (5) Optional— light fabric or tape wrapping of rib booms. (6) Rib boom. Dacron fabric more commonly used in America, could be doped to ribs, tensioned with warm iron.

Left: Types of ribs and spar sections. (A) Solid ply rib, flanges and local stiffening of spruce; hole for control lines (e.g. Fokker D.7). (B) Ply rib with lightening holes (elongated or circular) (e.g. Flying Flea). (C) Spruce or ash girder rib, ply gussets at joints, glued and/or pinned (e.g. Turbulent). (D) Built up rib with ply webs (e.g. Mosquito). Spars: (E) Solid spar. (F) Solid or laminated spar, lightened with spanwise channels. (G) Box spar, solid flanges, ply or laminated webs. (H) Box spar, laminated flanges, ply webs. (J) Typical steel longeron/former bracket, bracing wire linkages with adjustment turnbuckles. (K) Glued longeron/former joint, packing blocks and ply gussets for maximum glued surface.

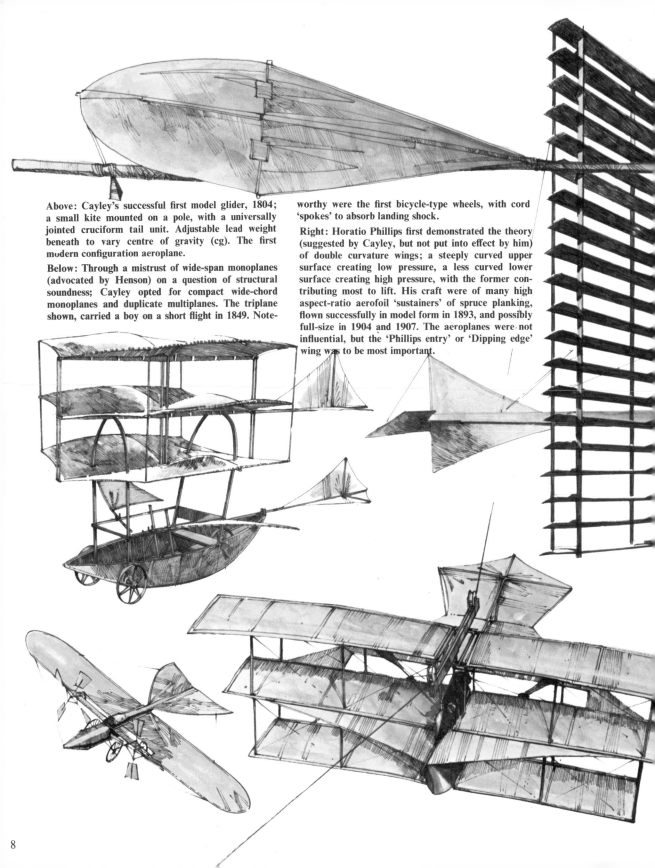

Above: Cayley's successful first model glider, 1804; a small kite mounted on a pole, with a universally jointed cruciform tail unit. Adjustable lead weight beneath to vary centre of gravity (cg). The first modern configuration aeroplane.

Below: Through a mistrust of wide-span monoplanes (advocated by Henson) on a question of structural soundness; Cayley opted for compact wide-chord monoplanes and duplicate multiplanes. The triplane shown, carried a boy on a short flight in 1849. Note-worthy were the first bicycle-type wheels, with cord 'spokes' to absorb landing shock.

Right: Horatio Phillips first demonstrated the theory (suggested by Cayley, but not put into effect by him) of double curvature wings; a steeply curved upper surface creating low pressure, a less curved lower surface creating high pressure, with the former contributing most to lift. His craft were of many high aspect-ratio aerofoil 'sustainers' of spruce planking, flown successfully in model form in 1893, and possibly full-size in 1904 and 1907. The aeroplanes were not influential, but the 'Phillips entry' or 'Dipping edge' wing was to be most important.

IN PRACTICE

INTRODUCTION

In the earliest days of aviation the choice of materials for construction was of less importance than in later years. Iron and steel were available, even aluminium from about the middle of the nineteenth century, but all were of considerably greater weight, and surrounded by far less understanding than the traditional material—wood. More fundamentally, the search was for the theoretical source of flight, the question of which materials were most suitable was to arise later.

There were many examples of excellent intuitive design failing for lack of a motor, or suitable materials. Others failed through an incomplete understanding of, or illogical disbelief in, known facts and natural phenomena. Da Vinci is an oft quoted example, but Cayley's was more unfortunate, as at the time of his death he was but two decades from the invention of the internal combustion engine, which would have made sound facts from his theories.

However, by the work that he did, Sir George Cayley can rightly be called the Father of modern avaiation. From a complete analysis of bird flight, fish and kites, he revealed the value of cambered wings, dihedral rudders and elevators, streamlining ('the body of least resistance'), pendulum stability and the need to divorce lift from thrust. On at least two occasions he launched manned gliders, and conducted the most complete practical experimentation to support theoretical findings. His papers were widely published in 1810, 1853 and 1876, and had a direct influence on the significant aviators of the nineteenth century, to Chanute, the Wright brothers and beyond.

To get the man and his work into perspective, however, one has to remember that much was done before 1810, at the height of the Napoleonic Wars; a time when the steam railway locomotive was barely out of its shell.

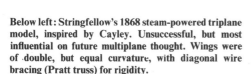

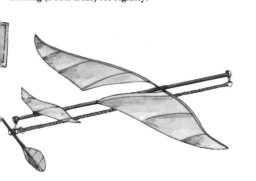

Below left: Stringfellow's 1868 steam-powered triplane model, inspired by Cayley. Unsuccessful, but most influential on future multiplane thought. Wings were of double, but equal curvature, with diagonal wire bracing (Pratt truss) for rigidity.

Far left: Victor Tatin's successful compressed-air driven model of 1879. This, like Henson's fictional Aerial Carriage, received widespread publicity in its day, keeping alive much needed effective propaganda as well as being most prophetic of modern tractor twin layouts.

Near left: Alphonse Penauds 'Planophore', 1871, the first rubber-motored model. Also, the first inherently stable aeroplane, with tailplane set at a negative angle of incidence and with turned-up wingtips creating a dihedral angle.

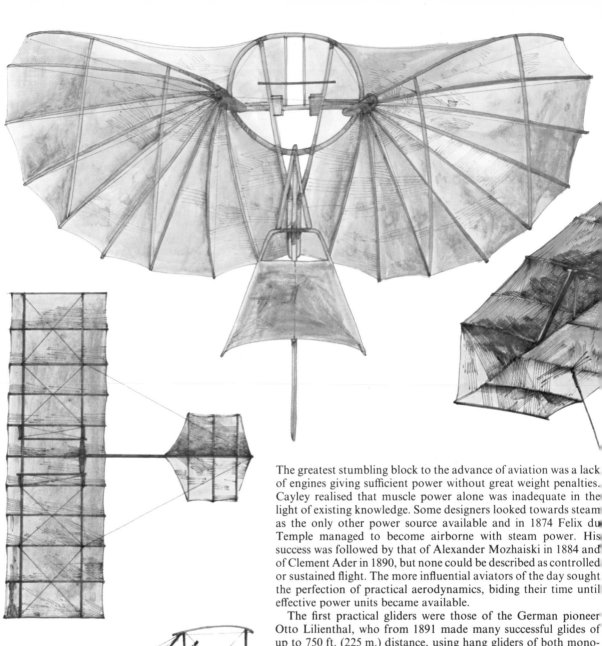

The greatest stumbling block to the advance of aviation was a lack of engines giving sufficient power without great weight penalties. Cayley realised that muscle power alone was inadequate in the light of existing knowledge. Some designers looked towards steam as the only other power source available and in 1874 Felix du Temple managed to become airborne with steam power. His success was followed by that of Alexander Mozhaiski in 1884 and of Clement Ader in 1890, but none could be described as controlled or sustained flight. The more influential aviators of the day sought the perfection of practical aerodynamics, biding their time until effective power units became available.

The first practical gliders were those of the German pioneer Otto Lilienthal, who from 1891 made many successful glides of up to 750 ft. (225 m.) distance, using hang gliders of both monoplane and biplane type. His craft were based on the work of Cayley, plus original research on bird-flight, but he was never convinced of the fallacy of ornithoptic flight, and returned to that theme with his design for a powered glider in 1896. His wings were of willow switches, covered with waxed linen fabric and wire-braced to vertical kingposts. His work caught the imagination of contemporary pioneers, and was copied by Pilcher, Ferber and Archdeacon in Europe, and Octave Chanute in America.

Chanute modified the principle to straight biplane wings, each of two solid spruce spars with ribs laid over at right-angles, thereby setting the pattern for future construction. Furthermore, in 1886 Daimler had launched the automobile with a four-stroke petrol engine; here at last was a motor with adequate power/weight ratio for a flying machine.

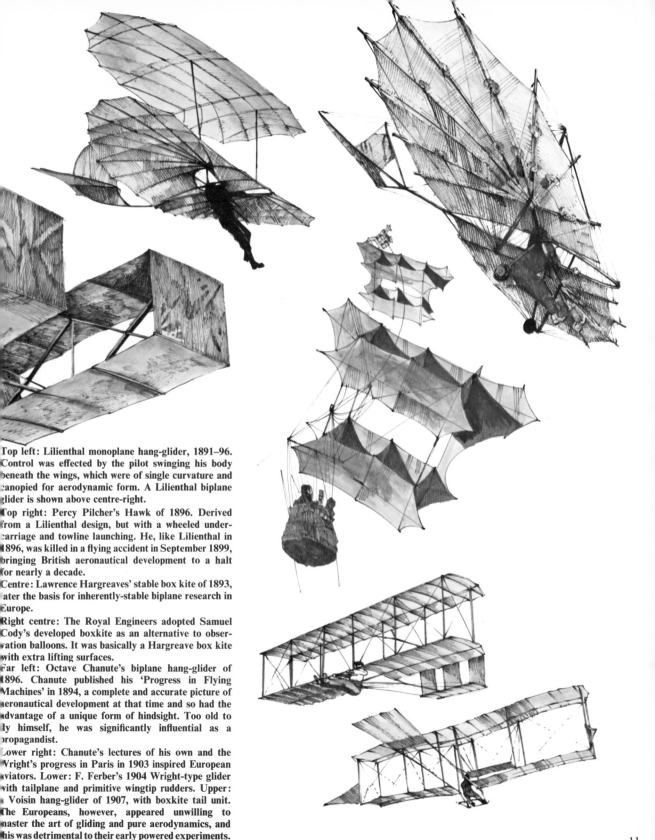

Top left: Lilienthal monoplane hang-glider, 1891–96. Control was effected by the pilot swinging his body beneath the wings, which were of single curvature and canopied for aerodynamic form. A Lilienthal biplane glider is shown above centre-right.

Top right: Percy Pilcher's Hawk of 1896. Derived from a Lilienthal design, but with a wheeled under-carriage and towline launching. He, like Lilienthal in 1896, was killed in a flying accident in September 1899, bringing British aeronautical development to a halt for nearly a decade.

Centre: Lawrence Hargreaves' stable box kite of 1893, later the basis for inherently-stable biplane research in Europe.

Right centre: The Royal Engineers adopted Samuel Cody's developed boxkite as an alternative to obser-vation balloons. It was basically a Hargreave box kite with extra lifting surfaces.

Far left: Octave Chanute's biplane hang-glider of 1896. Chanute published his 'Progress in Flying Machines' in 1894, a complete and accurate picture of aeronautical development at that time and so had the advantage of a unique form of hindsight. Too old to fly himself, he was significantly influential as a propagandist.

Lower right: Chanute's lectures of his own and the Wright's progress in Paris in 1903 inspired European aviators. Lower: F. Ferber's 1904 Wright-type glider with tailplane and primitive wingtip rudders. Upper: a Voisin hang-glider of 1907, with boxkite tail unit. The Europeans, however, appeared unwilling to master the art of gliding and pure aerodynamics, and this was detrimental to their early powered experiments.

The first heavier-than-air powered flight took place on December 17 1903 at Kitty Hawk, North Carolina. The craft was the Wright Flyer I, built by the brothers Wilbur and Orville Wright, and the flight lasted 12 seconds, covering 120 ft. (36·5 m.).

The Wrights received their greatest support from Octave Chanute, on whose hang-gliders their work was broadly based. This was, however, more a synthesis of known aerodynamic phenomena compounded by intuitive design, and was most thoroughly researched and effective in practice. They introduced the capability of complete control in the air by flexing the wings along their rear spars, activated by a system of piano wires running over pulleys and connected to a sliding hip cradle in which the pilot lay—the essence of which is indicated in Diagram B. Rear mounted rudders were linked to the warp system to maintain equilibrium in the turn and minimise the effects of side gusts. Elevators were mounted forward and were of single curvature, it being possible to reverse their camber, and thus accentuate their characteristics, in descending flight (diagram A). The horizontally mounted engine was Wright designed, employing a one-piece aluminium casting for cylinders and crankcase—the first of its kind. The propellors, of laminated spruce, were similarly home designed, and of a most advanced and efficient form. Transmission was via cycle chains (the brothers' former trade). The airframe was of Oregon Spruce, with solid spars and built-up ribs, with Ash frame/skid unit. Piano wire was employed for bracing, with chandelier chains where warp wires passed over pulleys.

The Wright machines changed little in appearance over the succeeding years—the pilot adopted a sitting position, engines of up to 35 h.p. (originally 12 h.p.) were fitted and warp controls received due modification. Even at the Rheims meeting in 1909 few others could compete with the Wright types for flying efficiency.

21
20
19

Right: Only competitor to the Wrights was S. P. Langley, astronomer and secretary of the Smithsonian Institution. In 1898 the U.S. Government financed him to build an aeroplane, based on a model of 1896 which flew a distance of 4,000 ft. (1,219 m.). The fuselage structure was of steel tube, power came from a 52 h.p. radial, span 48 ft. (14·6 m.). Two launches were attempted from a catapult on a houseboat on the Potomac river in 1903, but the craft was both aerodynamically and structurally deficient, breaking up on each occasion.

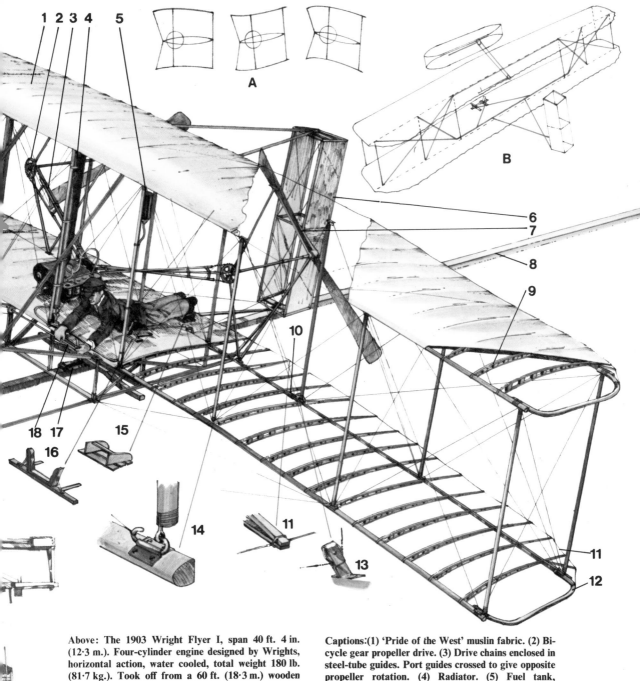

A

B

1 2 3 4   5

6
7
8
9
10
11
12
13
14
11
18 17
16
15

Above: The 1903 Wright Flyer I, span 40 ft. 4 in. (12·3 m.). Four-cylinder engine designed by Wrights, horizontal action, water cooled, total weight 180 lb. (81·7 kg.). Took off from a 60 ft. (18·3 m.) wooden rail, the aircraft mounted on a two-wheeled trolley. This was the basis of their later 'dropped-weight' assisted take-off system. Longest flight on December 17, 1903 was 59 seconds, covering 852 ft. (260 m.), the Flyer being badly damaged on landing. After repair it was stored; exhibited in the Science Museum, London, 1928–48; now in Smithsonian Institution, Washington D.C.

Captions:(1) 'Pride of the West' muslin fabric. (2) Bicycle gear propeller drive. (3) Drive chains enclosed in steel-tube guides. Port guides crossed to give opposite propeller rotation. (4) Radiator. (5) Fuel tank, one-third of a gallon (1·5 l.). (6) Double rudder/gust damper. (7) Laminated spruce propellers. (8) Launching rail. (9) Built-up ribs, ash flanges. (10) Hinge in rear spar to facilitate warping. (11) Wire trailing edge. (12) Spruce wing-tip bow, lashed to spars. (13) Warp-wire pulley. (14) Typical strut-spar linkage. (15) Foot-step. (16) Sliding hip cradle. (17) Launching trolley. (18) Elevator control. (19) Rail guide (bicycle-hub). (20) Ash frame-skid unit. (21) Spruce single curvature elevators.

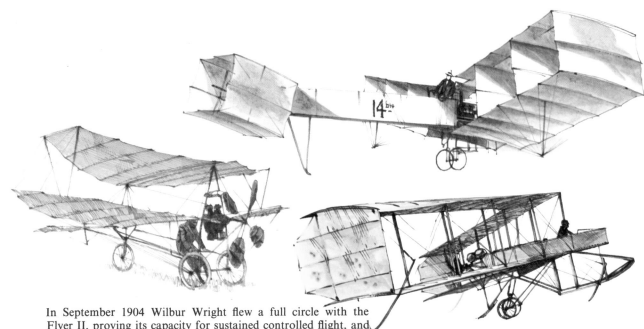

In September 1904 Wilbur Wright flew a full circle with the Flyer II, proving its capacity for sustained controlled flight, and confirming success of the warping system. Having, as they thought, mastered the art, his firm ceased flying in 1905, confident in their technical superiority.

In April 1903, Chanute lectured in Paris on the Wright's 1902 glider, on which the warp rudder control had been perfected, thus rejuvenating interest in European aviation, which had been dormant since Lilienthal's death. Many builders copied the basic Wright layout, although few understood its principles and none applied them correctly. Some adjusted the Wrights' design to their own ideas with moderate success. One such example was Ferber's 1904 glider, with a fixed tailplane fitted to biplane wings of steep dihedral.

This raises a major distinction between the Wright's ideas and those of other experimentors. In Europe Inherent-Stability was the goal, and they sought to perfect aeroplanes that would virtually look after themselves once in the air, with very little attention from the pilot. The Wright Flyers were deliberately unstable, requiring the control of a pilot as an integral part of the machine. Dihedral wings and a fixed tailplane bestowed on the machine a measure of lateral and longtitudinal stability, so despite, or perhaps because of, their misunderstanding of the Wrights' principles the Europeans were stumbling towards a better aerodynamic layout. a form already well proven by nineteenth century experimentors.

European progress towards powered flight was painfully slow; Santos Dumont flew tentatively in 1906, Voisin in 1907, but no one had conceived an effective control system, although ailerons were used with some measure of success. In November 1907 Henry Farman flew for just over one minute in a Voisin (the Wrights had flown for more than half an hour at a time in 1905) and travelled a complete circular course in January 1908—no doubt an uncomfortable affair, using rudders only, with power surges to regain control as the wings dipped and side-slipped.

However, the flying movement was at last getting somewhere, and gained momentum in August 1908, when Wilbur Wright flew in France, revealing the secret of effective control which was to revolutionise European aviation.

Above top: Santos Dumont 14bis, October 1906; boxkite screens, steep dihedral for stability, later with ailerons. Bamboo pole fuselage, pine wings, cotton covered.

Left: Ellehammer semi-biplane, September, 1906. Canvas kite-form wings, mahogany ribs, steel tube chassis.

Right: Dunne D.8, 1913. Inherently stable biplane 'flying wing'. Plywood nacelle, pine wings, linen fabric. Steel tube undercarriage.

Facing page, top: Voisin biplane, boxkite wing and tail, forward elevator. No lateral control (Farman fitted ailerons to one 1908). Ash framed wings, tail and nacelle, steel tube outrigger and sprung undercarriage. Ash struts with aluminium sockets. Continental fabric, piano wire bracing.

Right: Cody's Michelin cup machine, November 1910, 185 miles (298·5 km.) in 4 hr. 47 min. Bamboo fuselage, spruce wings, hickory struts and undercarriage, ailerons between wings. Pegamoid proofed linen.

Lower: C. Grahame-White developed Farman biplane, 1911, with ailerons, single tailplane, rudder. Ash outrigger, spruce wings, linen covered.

Foot: A. V. Roe's Avroplane or Bullseye, July 1909. Triangular section ash fuselage, apparently brown paper covered. Cotton-covered pine mainplanes acted as elevators.

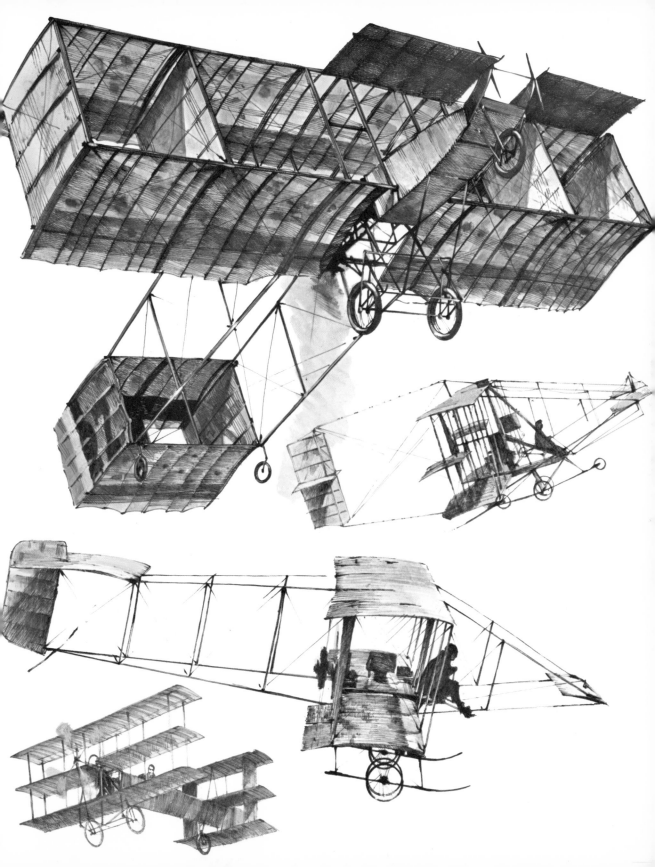

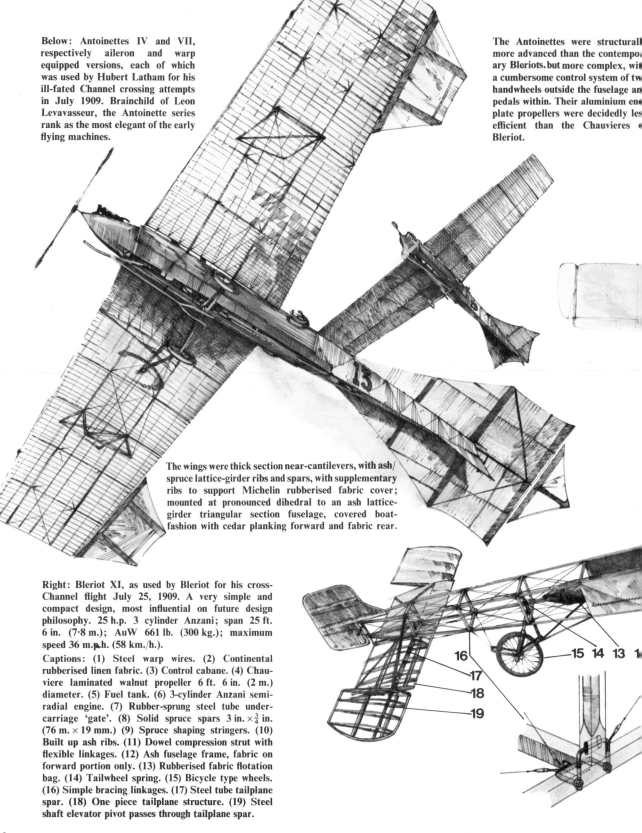

Below: Antoinettes IV and VII, respectively aileron and warp equipped versions, each of which was used by Hubert Latham for his ill-fated Channel crossing attempts in July 1909. Brainchild of Leon Levavasseur, the Antoinette series rank as the most elegant of the early flying machines.

The Antoinettes were structurally more advanced than the contemporary Bleriots, but more complex, with a cumbersome control system of two handwheels outside the fuselage and pedals within. Their aluminium end plate propellers were decidedly less efficient than the Chauvieres of Bleriot.

The wings were thick section near-cantilevers, with ash/spruce lattice-girder ribs and spars, with supplementary ribs to support Michelin rubberised fabric cover; mounted at pronounced dihedral to an ash lattice-girder triangular section fuselage, covered boat-fashion with cedar planking forward and fabric rear.

Right: Bleriot XI, as used by Bleriot for his cross-Channel flight July 25, 1909. A very simple and compact design, most influential on future design philosophy. 25 h.p. 3 cylinder Anzani; span 25 ft. 6 in. (7·8 m.); AuW 661 lb. (300 kg.); maximum speed 36 m.p.h. (58 km./h.).

Captions: (1) Steel warp wires. (2) Continental rubberised linen fabric. (3) Control cabane. (4) Chauviere laminated walnut propeller 6 ft. 6 in. (2 m.) diameter. (5) Fuel tank. (6) 3-cylinder Anzani semi-radial engine. (7) Rubber-sprung steel tube under-carriage 'gate'. (8) Solid spruce spars 3 in. × ¾ in. (76 m. × 19 mm.) (9) Spruce shaping stringers. (10) Built up ash ribs. (11) Dowel compression strut with flexible linkages. (12) Ash fuselage frame, fabric on forward portion only. (13) Rubberised fabric flotation bag. (14) Tailwheel spring. (15) Bicycle type wheels. (16) Simple bracing linkages. (17) Steel tube tailplane spar. (18) One piece tailplane structure. (19) Steel shaft elevator pivot passes through tailplane spar.

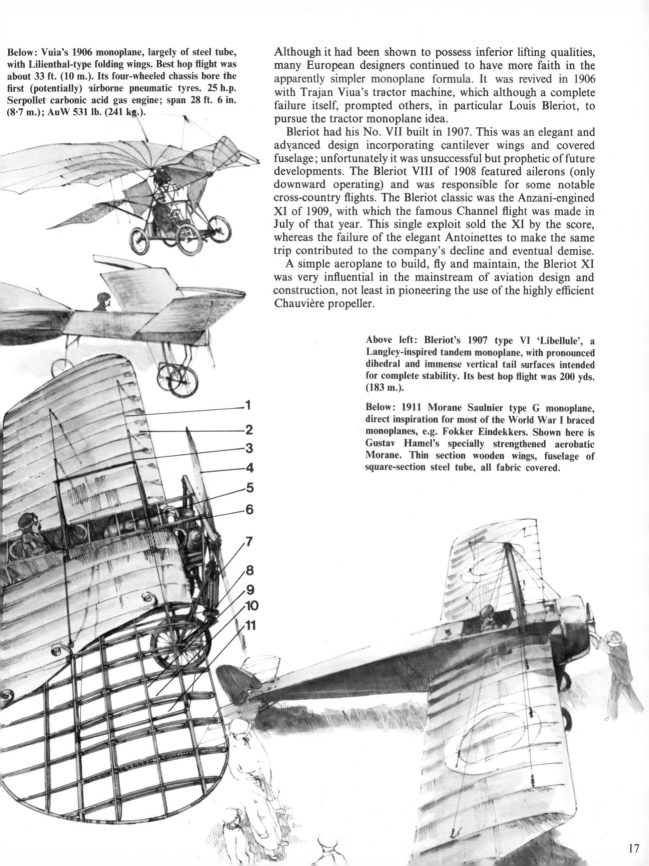

Below: Vuia's 1906 monoplane, largely of steel tube, with Lilienthal-type folding wings. Best hop flight was about 33 ft. (10 m.). Its four-wheeled chassis bore the first (potentially) airborne pneumatic tyres. 25 h.p. Serpollet carbonic acid gas engine; span 28 ft. 6 in. (8·7 m.); AuW 531 lb. (241 kg.).

Although it had been shown to possess inferior lifting qualities, many European designers continued to have more faith in the apparently simpler monoplane formula. It was revived in 1906 with Trajan Viua's tractor machine, which although a complete failure itself, prompted others, in particular Louis Bleriot, to pursue the tractor monoplane idea.

Bleriot had his No. VII built in 1907. This was an elegant and advanced design incorporating cantilever wings and covered fuselage; unfortunately it was unsuccessful but prophetic of future developments. The Bleriot VIII of 1908 featured ailerons (only downward operating) and was responsible for some notable cross-country flights. The Bleriot classic was the Anzani-engined XI of 1909, with which the famous Channel flight was made in July of that year. This single exploit sold the XI by the score, whereas the failure of the elegant Antoinettes to make the same trip contributed to the company's decline and eventual demise.

A simple aeroplane to build, fly and maintain, the Bleriot XI was very influential in the mainstream of aviation design and construction, not least in pioneering the use of the highly efficient Chauvière propeller.

Above left: Bleriot's 1907 type VI 'Libellule', a Langley-inspired tandem monoplane, with pronounced dihedral and immense vertical tail surfaces intended for complete stability. Its best hop flight was 200 yds. (183 m.).

Below: 1911 Morane Saulnier type G monoplane, direct inspiration for most of the World War I braced monoplanes, e.g. Fokker Eindekkers. Shown here is Gustav Hamel's specially strengthened aerobatic Morane. Thin section wooden wings, fuselage of square-section steel tube, all fabric covered.

1
2
3
4
5
6
7
8
9
10
11

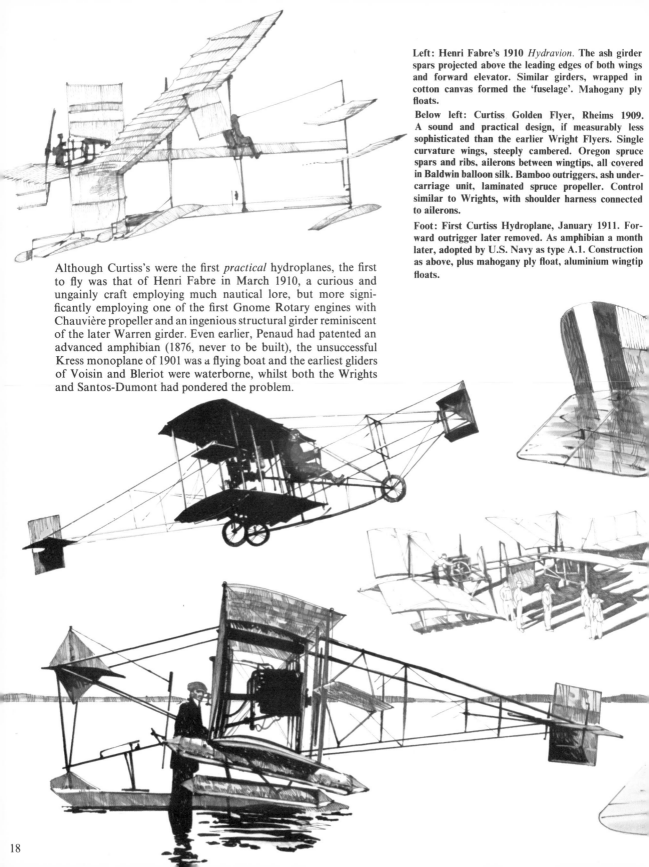

Left: Henri Fabre's 1910 *Hydravion.* **The ash girder spars projected above the leading edges of both wings and forward elevator. Similar girders, wrapped in cotton canvas formed the 'fuselage'. Mahogany ply floats.**

Below left: Curtiss Golden Flyer, Rheims 1909. A sound and practical design, if measurably less sophisticated than the earlier Wright Flyers. Single curvature wings, steeply cambered. Oregon spruce spars and ribs, ailerons between wingtips, all covered in Baldwin balloon silk. Bamboo outriggers, ash undercarriage unit, laminated spruce propeller. Control similar to Wrights, with shoulder harness connected to ailerons.

Foot: First Curtiss Hydroplane, January 1911. Forward outrigger later removed. As amphibian a month later, adopted by U.S. Navy as type A.1. Construction as above, plus mahogany ply float, aluminium wingtip floats.

Although Curtiss's were the first *practical* hydroplanes, the first to fly was that of Henri Fabre in March 1910, a curious and ungainly craft employing much nautical lore, but more significantly employing one of the first Gnome Rotary engines with Chauvière propeller and an ingenious structural girder reminiscent of the later Warren girder. Even earlier, Penaud had patented an advanced amphibian (1876, never to be built), the unsuccessful Kress monoplane of 1901 was a flying boat and the earliest gliders of Voisin and Bleriot were waterborne, whilst both the Wrights and Santos-Dumont had pondered the problem.

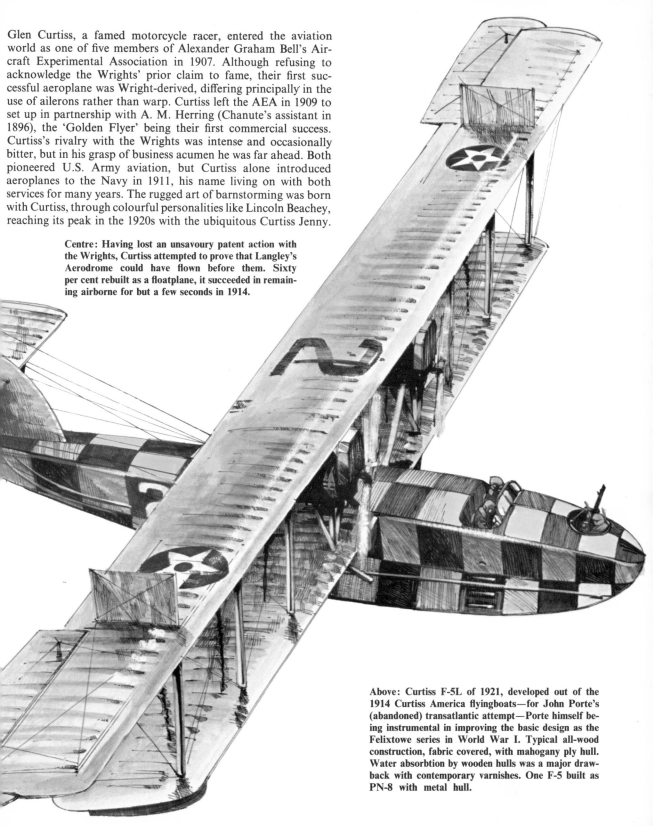

Glen Curtiss, a famed motorcycle racer, entered the aviation world as one of five members of Alexander Graham Bell's Aircraft Experimental Association in 1907. Although refusing to acknowledge the Wrights' prior claim to fame, their first successful aeroplane was Wright-derived, differing principally in the use of ailerons rather than warp. Curtiss left the AEA in 1909 to set up in partnership with A. M. Herring (Chanute's assistant in 1896), the 'Golden Flyer' being their first commercial success. Curtiss's rivalry with the Wrights was intense and occasionally bitter, but in his grasp of business acumen he was far ahead. Both pioneered U.S. Army aviation, but Curtiss alone introduced aeroplanes to the Navy in 1911, his name living on with both services for many years. The rugged art of barnstorming was born with Curtiss, through colourful personalities like Lincoln Beachey, reaching its peak in the 1920s with the ubiquitous Curtiss Jenny.

Centre: Having lost an unsavoury patent action with the Wrights, Curtiss attempted to prove that Langley's Aerodrome could have flown before them. Sixty per cent rebuilt as a floatplane, it succeeded in remaining airborne for but a few seconds in 1914.

Above: Curtiss F-5L of 1921, developed out of the 1914 Curtiss America flyingboats—for John Porte's (abandoned) transatlantic attempt—Porte himself being instrumental in improving the basic design as the Felixtowe series in World War I. Typical all-wood construction, fabric covered, with mahogany ply hull. Water absorbtion by wooden hulls was a major drawback with contemporary varnishes. One F-5 built as PN-8 with metal hull.

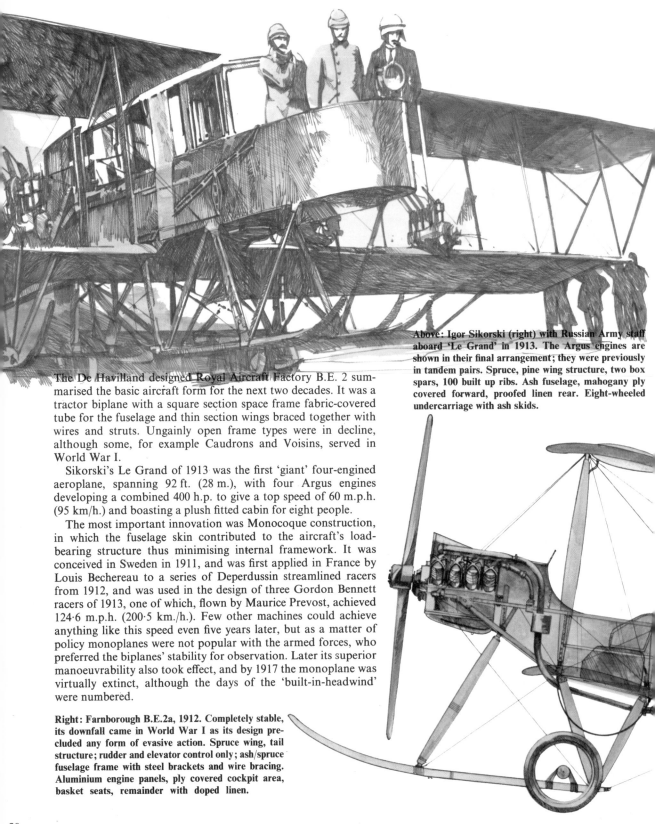

Above: Igor Sikorski (right) with Russian Army staff aboard 'Le Grand' in 1913. The Argus engines are shown in their final arrangement; they were previously in tandem pairs. Spruce, pine wing structure, two box spars, 100 built up ribs. Ash fuselage, mahogany ply covered forward, proofed linen rear. Eight-wheeled undercarriage with ash skids.

The De Havilland designed Royal Aircraft Factory B.E. 2 summarised the basic aircraft form for the next two decades. It was a tractor biplane with a square section space frame fabric-covered tube for the fuselage and thin section wings braced together with wires and struts. Ungainly open frame types were in decline, although some, for example Caudrons and Voisins, served in World War I.

Sikorski's Le Grand of 1913 was the first 'giant' four-engined aeroplane, spanning 92 ft. (28 m.), with four Argus engines developing a combined 400 h.p. to give a top speed of 60 m.p.h. (95 km/h.) and boasting a plush fitted cabin for eight people.

The most important innovation was Monocoque construction, in which the fuselage skin contributed to the aircraft's load-bearing structure thus minimising internal framework. It was conceived in Sweden in 1911, and was first applied in France by Louis Bechereau to a series of Deperdussin streamlined racers from 1912, and was used in the design of three Gordon Bennett racers of 1913, one of which, flown by Maurice Prevost, achieved 124·6 m.p.h. (200·5 km./h.). Few other machines could achieve anything like this speed even five years later, but as a matter of policy monoplanes were not popular with the armed forces, who preferred the biplanes' stability for observation. Later its superior manoeuvrability also took effect, and by 1917 the monoplane was virtually extinct, although the days of the 'built-in-headwind' were numbered.

Right: Farnborough B.E.2a, 1912. Completely stable, its downfall came in World War I as its design precluded any form of evasive action. Spruce wing, tail structure; rudder and elevator control only; ash/spruce fuselage frame with steel brackets and wire bracing. Aluminium engine panels, ply covered cockpit area, basket seats, remainder with doped linen.

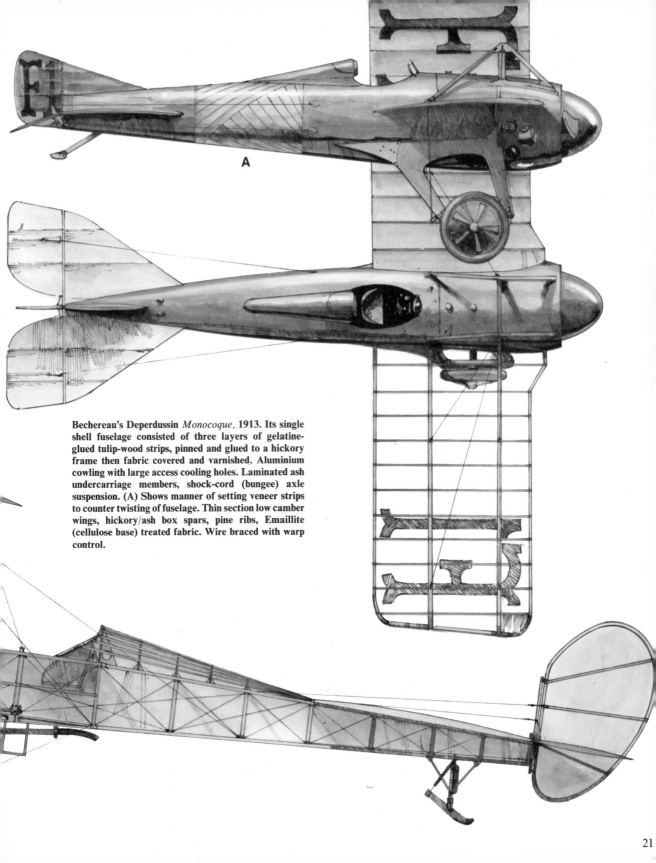

A

Bechereau's Deperdussin *Monocoque,* 1913. Its single shell fuselage consisted of three layers of gelatine-glued tulip-wood strips, pinned and glued to a hickory frame then fabric covered and varnished. Aluminium cowling with large access cooling holes. Laminated ash undercarriage members, shock-cord (bungee) axle suspension. (A) Shows manner of setting veneer strips to counter twisting of fuselage. Thin section low camber wings, hickory/ash box spars, pine ribs, Emaillite (cellulose base) treated fabric. Wire braced with warp control.

Right: Fokker D.7, possibly the best fighter scout of World War I, not fast, but manoeuvrable and with good altitude performance. Fabric of ply covered welded steel tube wire-braced fuselage. Thick one-piece cantilever wings, laminated pine/birch ply box spars and compression ribs, solid ply standard ribs. Ply covered leading edge, remainder fabric covered; ribs braced with spanwise rubber cord lattice. Wire trailing edge, giving characteristic scalloped edge. No dihedral or external wire bracing; steel tube interplane struts.

Inset: Prototype Fokker Dr.1, flown with pure cantilever wings, production types had one-piece interplane struts to counter flutter.

Right: Sopwith Camel, successor to Pup and Triplane. Five thousand built 1917–18. Succeeded by Snipe, with built up circular-section fuselage and double bay wings. Extremely manoeuvrable due to forward concentration of weight, and torque of rotary engine. Twin synchronised Vickers machineguns. Typical all wood, wire braced structure. Engines, various: 130 h.p. Clerget, 150 h.p. Bentley, 110 h.p. Le Rhone, 150 h.p. Monosoupape (in America); span 28 ft. (8·5 m.); AuW 1,453 lb. (659 kg.); maximum speed 113 m.p.h. (182 km./h.).

Captions: (1) Lightened plywood ribs, spruce flanges. (2) Solid compression ribs. (3) Interior bracing wires. (4) Solid streamline section struts. (5) Spruce/ply box spars. (6) Spruce leading edge. (7) PC 10 (pigmented celluose No. 10) doped linen fabric. (8) Basket seat. (9) Fuel tank. (10) Ash longerons. (11) Ply turtledeck formers. (12) Spruce compression members. (13) Rudder/elevator wires. (14) Diagonal box bracing. (15) Rudder control lever. (16) Elevator control linkage. (17) Ash skid with steel shoe, shock cord (bungeé) spring.

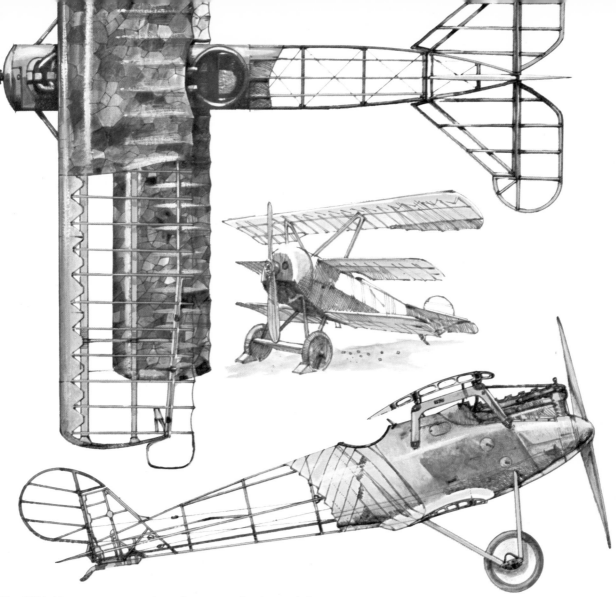

The 1914–18 war saw moves toward mass production and the standardisation of constructional methods. Wings varied little, consisting of two spruce or pine spars per wing with regularly spaced spruce and/or ply ribs, covered in doped fabric; Fokker's wings were cantilevers of deep section requiring no bracing wires and only light interplane struts. Fuselage forms were more diverse. The Allied powers rarely veered from the wood/wire/fabric formula—preferring to rely on the tried and proven than possibly waste time and money on alternatives at such a critical time. The Germans were more adventurous—Fokker used welded carbon-steel tube, generally mistrusted elsewhere, for greater convenience in production. Albatros and Pfalz went in for smoothly stream-lined forms, semi-monocoques of ply sheet pinned and glued to light formers (Albatros), or adapted from Deperdussin (Pfalz). All three forms, plus Fokker's wing were significant innovations of great importance in post-war development.

Above: Pfalz D.III, produced as an answer to the French Nieuport scouts, using a direct copy of their sesquiplane wing cellule. Monocoque fuselage shell built in two halves. Birch veneers with fabric stiffening strips, casein bonded, spruce sub-structure. Metal framed control surfaces; fabric covered wooden wing. Laminated ash one piece interplane struts. Excellent gun platform, high diving speed and strong under fire, but slower and less manoeuvrable in combat than con-temporaries due to greater weight of Wickelrumpf (wrapped fuselage).

Facing page, right: Also designed after Nieuport was the Albatros series. Oval section fuselage of formers and six stringers, ply and fabric covered. Lighter, more handy, and quicker in production than the Pfalz scouts.

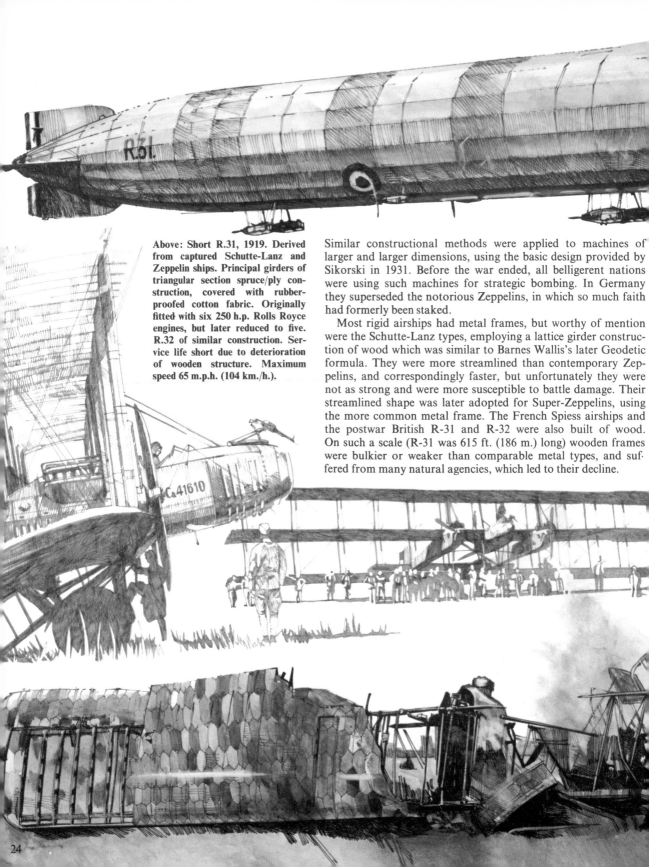

Above: Short R.31, 1919. Derived from captured Schutte-Lanz and Zeppelin ships. Principal girders of triangular section spruce/ply construction, covered with rubber-proofed cotton fabric. Originally fitted with six 250 h.p. Rolls Royce engines, but later reduced to five. R.32 of similar construction. Service life short due to deterioration of wooden structure. Maximum speed 65 m.p.h. (104 km./h.).

Similar constructional methods were applied to machines of larger and larger dimensions, using the basic design provided by Sikorski in 1931. Before the war ended, all belligerent nations were using such machines for strategic bombing. In Germany they superseded the notorious Zeppelins, in which so much faith had formerly been staked.

Most rigid airships had metal frames, but worthy of mention were the Schutte-Lanz types, employing a lattice girder construction of wood which was similar to Barnes Wallis's later Geodetic formula. They were more streamlined than contemporary Zeppelins, and correspondingly faster, but unfortunately they were not as strong and were more susceptible to battle damage. Their streamlined shape was later adopted for Super-Zeppelins, using the more common metal frame. The French Spiess airships and the postwar British R-31 and R-32 were also built of wood. On such a scale (R-31 was 615 ft. (186 m.) long) wooden frames were bulkier or weaker than comparable metal types, and suffered from many natural agencies, which led to their decline.

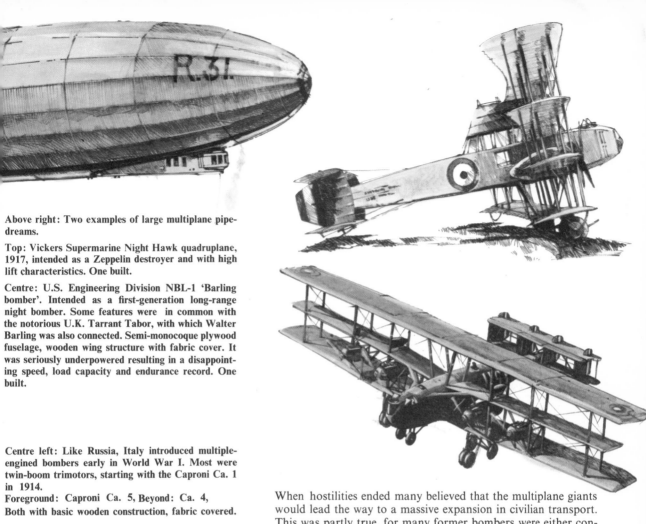

Above right: Two examples of large multiplane pipe-dreams.

Top: Vickers Supermarine Night Hawk quadruplane, 1917, intended as a Zeppelin destroyer and with high lift characteristics. One built.

Centre: U.S. Engineering Division NBL-1 'Barling bomber'. Intended as a first-generation long-range night bomber. Some features were in common with the notorious U.K. Tarrant Tabor, with which Walter Barling was also connected. Semi-monocoque plywood fuselage, wooden wing structure with fabric cover. It was seriously underpowered resulting in a disappointing speed, load capacity and endurance record. One built.

Centre left: Like Russia, Italy introduced multiple-engined bombers early in World War I. Most were twin-boom trimotors, starting with the Caproni Ca. 1 in 1914.
Foreground: Caproni Ca. 5, **Beyond:** Ca. 4, Both with basic wooden construction, fabric covered.

Below: Wrecked Gotha G. V, 1918, exposing general wing structure. Typical ash/spruce/ply, wire braced and fabric covered. Steel tube fuselage and tail unit.

When hostilities ended many believed that the multiplane giants would lead the way to a massive expansion in civilian transport. This was partly true, for many former bombers were either converted, or their designs adapted for passenger operations. Their use was limited to about a decade, mainly because for their size their lifting capacity was small, and their standard of comfort was low. Their 'built in headwinds' kept their speed so low that airships still provided valid competition. The real answer to bulk passenger transport eventually came from smaller aircraft, where monocoque construction was able to show its true value in terms of lightness and speed.

THE POOR RELATION

INTRODUCTION

The end of hostilities led to a massive run-down of production, and almost brought to an end the use of the aeroplane as a fighting machine. In Britain, new military production did not really get under way until 1924, during which time the only real advance in design was from rotary to radial engines. Under a report of 1921 it was officially decreed that in the production for military orders metal would be used instead of wood. The decision was a strategic one, since timber for spars and other parts was not grown in Britain and was difficult to store in quantity, and its delivery had, during World War I, been made difficult by U-boat blockades, which interrupted supplies from North America. The raw material for metal construction on the other hand was available locally and also presented fewer problems in storage. High-strength alloy steel and aluminium were introduced and used in folded or rolled sheet form to retain strength and rigidity under stress and compression within the weight limitations of former wooden types, ordinary steel being some eighteen times heavier than an equivalent volume of spruce. In the R.A.F.'s case the form of construction was identical to that in which wood had been used, little use being made of the materials inherent qualities, a condition that persisted into the 1930s.

Elsewhere the supply problem was less critical, e.g. wooden wings were the norm for U.S. military aircraft until the Grumman 'Barrels' from 1931. Fuselages were successively of fabric-covered welded steel tube, built-up aluminium and eventually of full duralumin monocoque.

In the civil field similar conditions applied. The Handley-Page 42 of 1931 was a large all-metal biplane, little in advance of the wooden types of the early 1920s, whilst Fokker extended the wood and steel theme of WWI into a most successful series of monoplane transports.

As well as providing an excellent streamlined form, the monocoque type of fuselage offered the whole of its interior, uncluttered by stays or wires, for capacity transport. To apply streamlining to the older form of construction necessitated the build up of a near circular section with stringers and fabric around the square space-frame thereby increasing bulk without improving interior space. Lockheeds took advantage of this for the excellent Vega of 1927, from which the modern concept of high speed transportation has evolved, i.e. clean and uncluttered in external line, but offering maximum internal capacity for passenger accommodation.

Right: Lockheed Vega model 5; the 'Winnie Mae', used by aviator Wiley Post with Harold Gatty for two round the world records. Conceived by A. Loughhead, J. Northrop and D. Douglas (later of fame in their own right) in 1926. First flight July 1927, total cost of prototype and tooling $17,500 (approximately £4,000). Many famous flyers, including Amelia Earhart, Charles Lindbergh, Roscoe Turner and Sir Hubert Wilkins chose Lockheed types for distance flights.

Fuselage construction was derived broadly from Deperdussin/Pfalz practice, three ply birch monocoque built up in concrete mould, veneers alternately diagonally and longitudinally laid. Casein glue used throughout, set at 25 lb./sq. in. pressure under inflated rubber bag. Finally doped and polished. Doors, etc. cut from shell. Whole fuselage from engine bulkhead to tailcone including fin built in two half units, joined along centreline, pinned and glued to internal formers and stringers of spruce. All wood one-piece cantilever, two-spar torsion box wing with polished stressed ply skin.

Nearly 200 'Plywood bullets' built by Lockheed—8 parasol wing Air Express, 14 Sirius, 6 Altair, 35 Orion, but the bulk were Vegas—128—including one with duralumin fuselage. Price in 1928 $13,500 (approximately £3,000); 450 h.p. Wasp (model 1—220 h.p. Wright Whirlwind); span 41 ft. (12.5 m.); AuW 4,270 lb. (1,937 kg.); maximum speed 185 m.p.h. (241 km./h.).

Facing page, centre: Two examples of U.K. light/medium transports, using all-wood stressed-skin construction for smooth aerodynamic finish and convenience in small scale production. Right: Percival Q. 6 Petrel 1937; two-spar torsion-box wing, spruce girder ribs with diagonal bracing struts, thus eliminating wire bracing. Ply box streamlined fuselage, with stringers and fabric. Fastest 'plane in its class pre-war.

Left: Airspeed Envoy, 1935; the second commercial type introduced after the similar single-motor Courier, to embody a retractable undercarriage. An example from the King's flight is shown. Semi-monocoque stressed-ply fuselage with a luxury eight-seat cabin.

Lower: CANT (Cantieri Riceniti dell'Adriatico) Z506A of Ala Littoria. All wood stressed-skin construction, as were the majority of Italian transports of this vintage. Duralumin floats and struts, designed to be operable from unsettled water formed the basis of the war-time Z506B floatplane torpedo bomber.

Lockheeds followed the Vega with the parasol Mailplane, the two-place Sirius (to Lindbergh's specification), and finally the Orion before entering the all-metal school with the twin-engined Electra. The Orion had a duralumin monocoque fuselage, but retained a low wooden wing which accommodated a fully retractable undercarriage. European authorities were at first sceptical of the performance claims of Lockheed, but when Orions appeared in Europe under the Swissair flag, they were quick to forget their scepticism.

In Europe, wood remained as a more acceptable medium for construction of the small to medium capacity civil airliners right through the 1930s. Generally speaking, the higher cost all-metal types went to Government or to large operators where cost was either less important or more easily borne. Production line wages were still sufficiently low to prevent the comparatively large number of manhours per wooden airframe from becoming an economic burden, whilst the raw material was inexpensive and easily available.

The advantage of metal in small scale quantity production was ably demonstrated by the construction of the Piper Cub. The wing had spruce/ply box spars, but the ribs were stamped and assembled from aluminium alloy sheet making a great saving in both time and overall expense. Wood, by comparison, was certainly not the best medium for automated mass production.

Having successfully removed most of his plant and design staff from Germany to his native Holland prior to the 1919 armistice being drawn up, Anthony Fokker once more set up in business. For the next twenty years his characteristic high-wing transports were to be found throughout the world, but their popularity was soon to be eclipsed by the rush for all-metal types such as the DC-3 and Lockheed Electra, which were available from America in the late thirties. His designs were a natural extension of the D-7 having wooden cantilevered wings with a steel tube and fabric fuselages. Two examples, from different periods, of the Fokker boom are shown: Bottom: Fokker T-2 (F IV) of U.S. Army transcontinental flight, 1922. Centre: 1936 F-36, the only machine of its type.

Below: One of the first modern European designs to incorporate new American developments was the Heinkel He. 70, ostensibly a high-speed courier and mailplane, but soon developed into a high-speed light bomber. It had a cantilevered wooden wing with highly polished stressed-ply skin and a flush-riveted duralumin monocoque fuselage.

Below: 1935 Potez 62 of Air France. In widespread service, Inter-Europe, Paris–Saigon, Trans Andean, carrying fourteen passengers in two cabins. It sported two spar all-metal wings braced to the engine mounts and had a fuselage of square section, with four spruce longerons, ply covered on all faces. The fuselage sides were stiffened with internal vertical stringers and longitudinal stringers on the outside. The elevation profile of its fuselage was intended to duplicate the wing section in order to minimise drag. The wooden tail unit had fabric covered control surfaces. The combination of metal wings and a wooden fuselage was a somewhat rare form of composite construction.

1925 Schneider trophy Curtiss R3C-2,
with pilot—Lieut. 'Jimmy' Dolittle. Curtiss
shell construction, spruce fuselage frame, cross laminated birch veneer skin, first used on Curtiss 18B-T in
1918. Fabric covered wooden wings with surface
radiators, laminated 'I' form struts. Duralumin floats.
As landplane for 1925 Pulitzer race to 249 m.p.h.
(401 km./h.).

Although the air forces of the world were deep in the doldrums in
the early 1920s, many significant speed, endurance, height and
distance records were set up, especially in America. Official
interest in the Air Service may have decreased, but there was still
sufficient enthusiasm within the Service itself, and ingenuity
existed among the manufacturers to make the most of it. Both the
Schneider Trophy and Pulitzer prize competitions allowed ample
opportunity to pit the finesse of structural and engine design against
the clock in the quest for pure speed. Curtiss had built the models
18T and B for the Army and Navy respectively in 1918, each with
a finely streamlined monocoque fuselage. From 1921 the same
structure was employed in a series of racers for both Pulitzer and
Schneider, fitted respectively with wheels and floats, culminating
in the Navy R3C-2, which won the 1925 Schneider trophy at
232·5 m.p.h. (374 km./h.).

Wood or composite construction continued to be first choice
for sport or racing 'planes; most were one-off designs, taking
advantage of low material cost, minimal plant and tooling
requirements, and the smooth finish which at that time was only
possible with a wooden surface. Most were at the forefront of
current aerodynamic theory, and were often influential to later
design and constructional practice. For similar reasons wood has
been used for many research or experimental machines, including
the M2-F1 development glider for the recent NASA wingless
lifting-body re-entry vehicle programme.

Right, top to bottom: Granville Bros. Gee Bee model Z. First of Gee Bee 'all-engine' racers. Construction typical for the period, fabric covered steel-tube fuselage, wooden wings. Crashed spectacularly during landplane record attempt December 1931.

Second DH 88 Comet, flown as G-ACSR to fourth place in 1934 MacRobertson race. See p. 40.

Gunther Bros. Baumer Sausewind, foretelling shape of later Heinkel bombers. Successful entrant for 1925 Rundflug. Lightplane speed record of 133 m.p.h. (213 km./h.), October 1928. Plywood monocoque fuselage, fabric covered cantilever wings.

Hughes H-1, a most prophetic design of 1934. Apparently two different wing structures employed, the first of wooden spar and ribs, with ply skin—laid down 1 in. (25 mm.) thick, shaved down to $\frac{1}{8}$ in. (3 mm.) to give perfect surface contours. Later with similar structure but flush riveted duralumin skin. Dural monocoque fuselage. Very efficient retractable under-carriage. Crashed September 1935 during attempt at landplane speed record. In January 1937, crossed United States in 7 hrs. $28\frac{1}{2}$ min., at average speed of 332 m.p.h. (531 km./h.), with Hughes at controls. Like the H-4 Hercules (see p. 33), the H-1 is preserved.

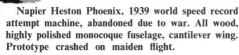

Napier Heston Phoenix, 1939 world speed record attempt machine, abandoned due to war. All wood, highly polished monocoque fuselage, cantilever wing. Prototype crashed on maiden flight.

Facing page.

Centre: Early Cierva autogiro, Avro 504K fuselage and engine, stub wings on tubular extensions. Fabric covered rotor blades with metal shafts and wooden ribs.

Lower: Miles M.35 Libellula, canard naval fighter project to provide low landing speed for aircraft-carriers, wingform virtually unstallable. Built in six weeks, flown May 1942. Developed into M.39 experimental bomber. Typical Miles all-wood structure, Magister undercarriage units.

Foot: Bristol 138A, high altitude research, established record of 53,937 ft. (1,6440 m.) in June 1937. All wood structure, ply/fabric covered.

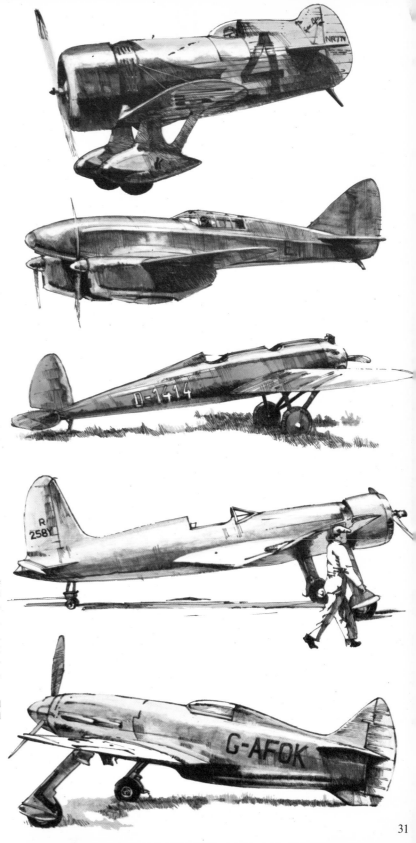

Facing page, upper: Fairchild AT-21 Gunner, six-man crew trainer. Spruce/compreg box spars, ribs; steel tube forward, spruce rear-fuselage frame—all Duramold skinned.

Lower: Andover Kent Langley monoplane, plastic moulding demonstrator. Wing in five integrally moulded units, fuselage in three. Engine cowlings/firewall of plastic ply/asbestos sandwich. Surfaces polished to reveal veneer finish. Two built 1940.

Something of a revolution occurred in aeroplane construction about the mid-1930s. All-metal stressed skin construction entered the world's air forces *en masse*, in parallel with widespread rearmament following the abortive League of Nations disarmament programme. For the wooden planemaker, synthetic resin cements of urea- and phenol-formaldehyde type appeared on the market.

The potential of these plastics was immense. Glue had always presented a problem; animal glues were not water or fungus-proof, and often inherently weak from uneven setting. Casein, a dairy by-product, was not gap filling and subject to mould. Resin cements however were unaffected by moisture, capable of prolonged immersion in water, and completely resistant to shrinkage, mould, fungi and micro-organisms of every description. They were used extensively in the manufacture of waterproof plywood, which was completely impregnated, and used in the construction of small boats and barrels.

The Finnish Halila company introduced their Jic process into Britain in 1934, inspiring De Havilland's Redux sandwich construction. Impregnation (impreg) and compression (compreg) gave plywood the versatility of sheet alloy, with greater margins of economy, but with greater weight. It was substantially more stable than metal, requiring less stiffening support, presenting a perfectly smooth finish without rivet heads. In America a number of patents were issued for the process, under the names Vidal, Durafoil, Duramold, etc., each represented by an experimental

prototype, which would have held considerable promise in the mass-produced light-twin market, had it not been for the onset of war. Duramold, developed by Col. Virginius Clark, was most widely accepted. Dry veneers were laid over a die, impregnated with plastic and subjected to a pressure up to 4,000 lb./sq. in. at 182°C., to give material of varying density which was varied according to the in-flight stress to which it was to be exposed. Fairchild took over Duramold in 1939, and built the successful AT-21 Gunner to this formula for the U.S.A.A.F. It was also adopted by Howard Hughes for his D-2 high altitude project (eventually as XF-11, but in light alloy), and H-4 Hercules flying boat, to date the largest airframe ever built, and living testimony to the possibilities of large wooden structures.

Below: Hughes H-4 Hercules ('Spruce Goose'). Fantastic in size, lifting capacity and development; was conceived in 1942, effectively as a flying Liberty ship, with capacity for 700 troops. Birch ply construction, using Diathermy, a radio frequency heating system, to bond huge Duramold planels. Eight tons saved by extracting pins from panels after gluing. Built in vast wooden hangar with eight-acre floor area at Culver city, towed 28 miles in three parts to Long Beach for assembly and launching. Flew one mile November 2, 1947 on third taxiing trial, its only flight whence it was hangared at Long Beach, California, where it remains, reputedly airworthy, to this day. Eight 3,000 h.p. Pratt & Whitney Wasp Major engines; span 320 ft. (97·69 m.); estimated AuW 400,000 lb. (18,436 kg.); estimated maximum speed 218 m.p.h. (350·83 km./h.).

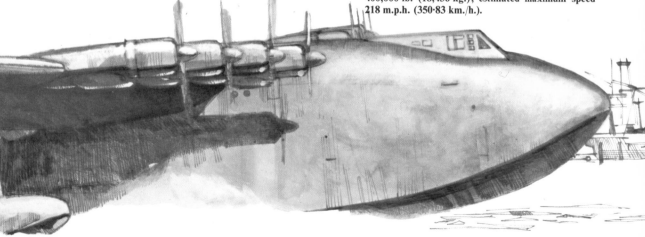

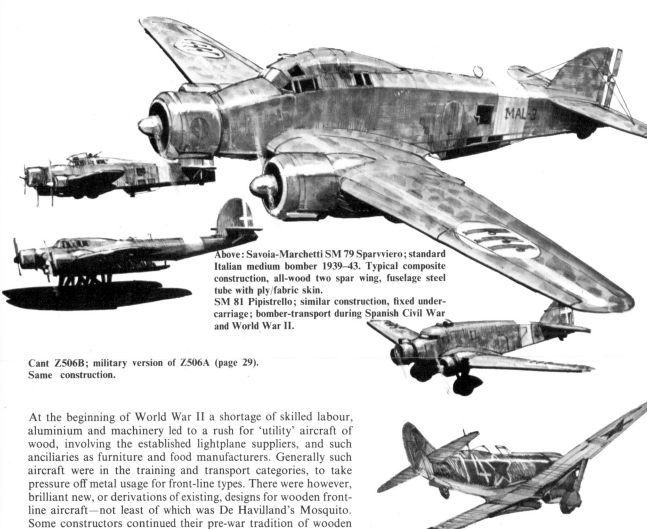

Above: Savoia-Marchetti SM 79 Sparvviero; standard Italian medium bomber 1939–43. Typical composite construction, all-wood two spar wing, fuselage steel tube with ply/fabric skin.
SM 81 Pipistrello; similar construction, fixed undercarriage; bomber-transport during Spanish Civil War and World War II.

Cant Z506B; military version of Z506A (page 29). Same construction.

At the beginning of World War II a shortage of skilled labour, aluminium and machinery led to a rush for 'utility' aircraft of wood, involving the established lightplane suppliers, and such anciliaries as furniture and food manufacturers. Generally such aircraft were in the training and transport categories, to take pressure off metal usage for front-line types. There were however, brilliant new, or derivations of existing, designs for wooden front-line aircraft—not least of which was De Havilland's Mosquito. Some constructors continued their pre-war tradition of wooden aeroplanes, e.g. Savoia Marchetti, Cant in Italy, and Caudron in France, whose 714 series of light fighters, derived from a 1935 Coup Deutsche racer, achieved a measure of operational success prior to the German invasion and later with Finnish forces, whose own indigenous designs were primarily of wood. Finland, possessor of great ingenuity, if not of material sophistication, also put in hand plans to convert existing designs to wooden construction, a single wooden Brewster Buffalo being built before their war with Russia ceased in 1944. Similarly Japan built a single wooden Nakajima Ki 84 Hayate as the Ki 106, marginally faster, but 600 lb. heavier. Most Russian fighters built during the war were of composite construction. Russia, like Finland, possessed vast timber resources, but had to import most of her light metal requirements.

In fact the expected shortages in labour and materials were less critical than expected and many of the stop-gap designs did not achieve production. Furthermore the mistakes of the twenties were manifested in reverse—metal techniques were often transposed directly into wood, without sufficient regard for the inherent qualities of each medium, resulting in unnecessarily bulky or heavy structures, with obvious penalties to overall performance.

Lavochkin La-5, 1943. Phenol-formaldehyde compreg construction, spars of compressed laminated birch, 6 mm. birch veneer skin, similarly monocoque fuselage.

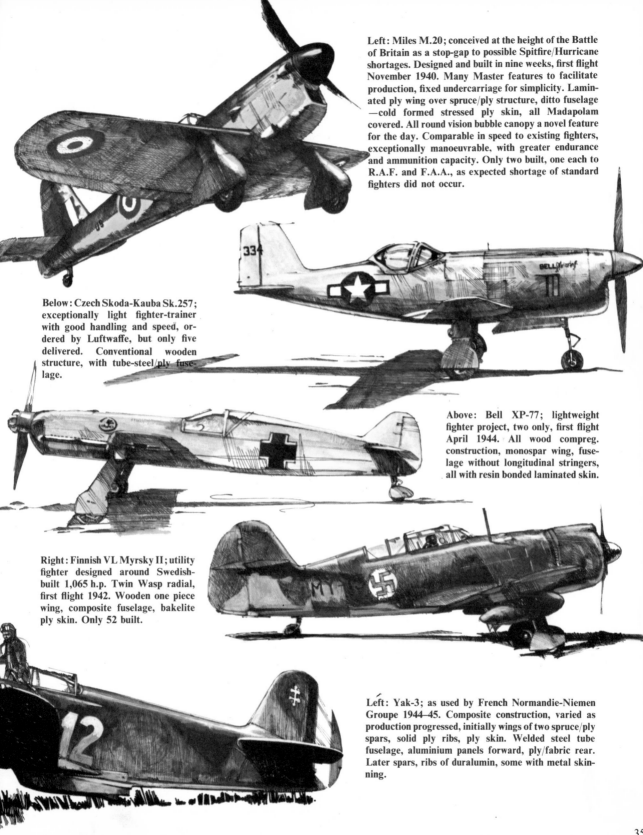

Left: Miles M.20; conceived at the height of the Battle of Britain as a stop-gap to possible Spitfire/Hurricane shortages. Designed and built in nine weeks, first flight November 1940. Many Master features to facilitate production, fixed undercarriage for simplicity. Laminated ply wing over spruce/ply structure, ditto fuselage —cold formed stressed ply skin, all Madapolam covered. All round vision bubble canopy a novel feature for the day. Comparable in speed to existing fighters, exceptionally manoeuvrable, with greater endurance and ammunition capacity. Only two built, one each to R.A.F. and F.A.A., as expected shortage of standard fighters did not occur.

Below: Czech Skoda-Kauba Sk.257; exceptionally light fighter-trainer with good handling and speed, ordered by Luftwaffe, but only five delivered. Conventional wooden structure, with tube-steel/ply fuselage.

Above: Bell XP-77; lightweight fighter project, two only, first flight April 1944. All wood compreg. construction, monospar wing, fuselage without longitudinal stringers, all with resin bonded laminated skin.

Right: Finnish VL Myrsky II; utility fighter designed around Swedish-built 1,065 h.p. Twin Wasp radial, first flight 1942. Wooden one piece wing, composite fuselage, bakelite ply skin. Only 52 built.

Left: Yak-3; as used by French Normandie-Niemen Groupe 1944–45. Composite construction, varied as production progressed, initially wings of two spruce/ply spars, solid ply ribs, ply skin. Welded steel tube fuselage, aluminium panels forward, ply/fabric rear. Later spars, ribs of duralumin, some with metal skinning.

(A) Boeing-Stearman Kaydet. Primary trainer. 10,000 plus built 1936–42. Steel tube fuselage, wooden wing, fabric covered. (B) Cessna AT-8 Bobcat. Crew trainer and utility transport. 5,000 built 1941–43, some from Canada as CCF Crane. Steel tube fuselage, wooden wing, fabric covered. (C) Avro (Federal) Anson. Canadian built, using Vidal moulded panels over steel tube frame. Wooden wing with bakelite-ply skin. 3,000 built 1941–43. With USAAF as AT-20. (D) Miles Master. Advanced trainer. All wooden stressed skin structure (as for Miles M.20 p.35). 3,000 built of all marks 1939–42. (E) Miles Magister. Basic trainer. All wood, ply and fabric covered. 1,200 built 1937–41.

(F) Airspeed Oxford. Crew trainer and ambulance. Derived from Envoy (p.29). All wood structure, stressed ply skin. 9,000 built 1937–44. **(G) Bucker Jungmeister.** Single place aerobatic trainer. Wooden wing, steel tube fuselage, fabric covered. With Luftwaffe from 1936. Postwar favourite for aerobatic displays. **(H) Fieseler Storch.** Observation type, famous for its STOL performance and low stalling speed. Wooden wings, steel tube fuselage, fabric covered. 2,500 built 1936–44.

The war resulted in the private pilot's pleasure craft becoming trainer aircraft, and the businessman's light twin a utility transport. Current constructional techniques were continued, some designs being adapted to all-wood construction where economy could be proved, e.g. Avro Ansons built in Canada. New types specifically for wood construction were introduced, although the new fully moulded types did not achieve quite the production success imagined for them, partly through misunderstanding of the material at design stages and partly due to fixed plant requirements—dies, thermal presses, etc., which complicated production procedures. Simple single-curvature stressed-ply panels or fabric cover proved more acceptable for speed of construction, despite inferior weather resistance—in any case, a long service life was not expected of such types. Resin glues were used almost universally.

Heavy transport types were mostly of all metal construction, but heavy gliders, intended to extend the useful capacity of existing transports and as an inexpensive means to deliver mass troop concentrations, were almost exclusively of wood. First used were German DFS 230 gliders in Belgium, 1940 and Crete, 1941. Later, Allied gliders spearheaded the Normandy invasion, and provided essential life-lines to troops in many sectors, notably in Burma. Extensive development resulted in the capacity to transport tanks and artillery (GAL Hamilcar, Messerschmitt 321). Powered gliders, providing extra range, achieved a measure of success, e.g. Messerschmitt's 323 Gigant, but were generally a poor compromise. The troop-gliders introduced a new dimension to wooden construction, that of the 'throwaway' aeroplane, later extended in Germany as a last ditch defensive measure.

Below left: Airspeed Horsa, troop glider, 30-man capacity; all wood, ply covered fuselage, ply/fabric covered wings. Main undercarriage dropped at takeoff in service, rear fuselage detachable on some.

Lower: Waco CG-4A Hadrian; 13,909 built by sixteen manufacturers, 1942–44. 15-seat capacity. Wooden wings, steel tube fuselage, fabric covered. Two side doors, hinged nose to facilitate loading.

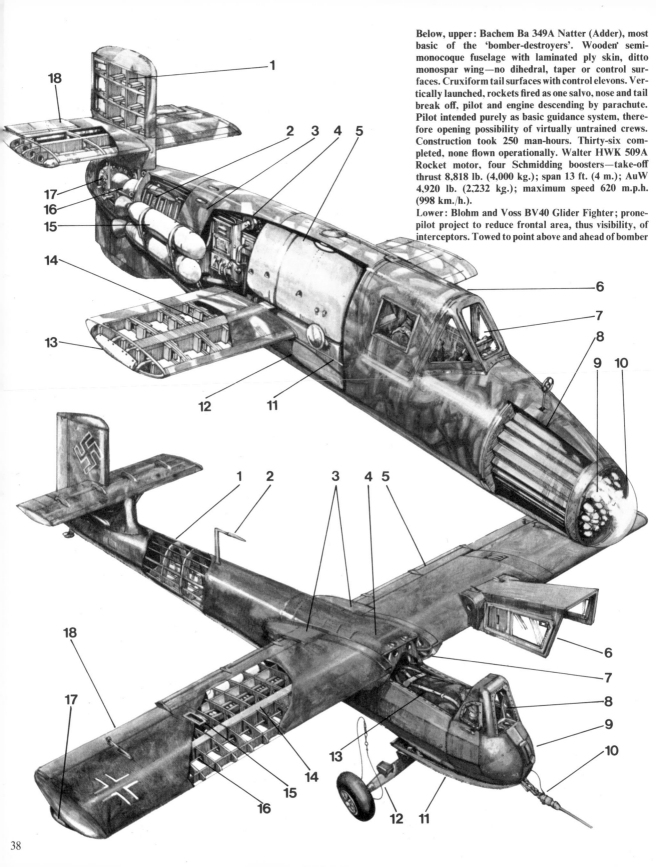

Below, upper: Bachem Ba 349A Natter (Adder), most basic of the 'bomber-destroyers'. Wooden' semi-monocoque fuselage with laminated ply skin, ditto monospar wing—no dihedral, taper or control surfaces. Cruxiform tail surfaces with control elevons. Vertically launched, rockets fired as one salvo, nose and tail break off, pilot and engine descending by parachute. Pilot intended purely as basic guidance system, therefore opening possibility of virtually untrained crews. Construction took 250 man-hours. Thirty-six completed, none flown operationally. Walter HWK 509A Rocket motor, four Schmidding boosters—take-off thrust 8,818 lb. (4,000 kg.); span 13 ft. (4 m.); AuW 4,920 lb. (2,232 kg.); maximum speed 620 m.p.h. (998 km./h.).

Lower: Blohm and Voss BV40 Glider Fighter; prone-pilot project to reduce frontal area, thus visibility, of interceptors. Towed to point above and ahead of bomber

As in World War I, Germany was more receptive to radical or unorthodox innovations than the Allies, and were consequently the first to operate turbo-jet and rocket powered aeroplanes. Despite these advantages, the sheer weight of the Allied bombing offensive from mid-1943 gradually wore down production capacity of conventional fighters, exacerbating the appalling attrition of operational types in combat.

Completely rethinking the fundamental tactics of interception, a scheme for 'bomber-destroyers' was launched, machines of small size, short duration but high fire-power and of simple construction using low priority materials to exploit the widest possible labour resources. Arriving too late in the war to be of any effect, and constantly bedevilled by official diffidence, as well as the radical, and therefore untried, nature of their design, few such aircraft were built and fewer still became operational. Nevertheless, they provided a most fascinating, if short lived and lethal, era in aviation history.

stream by fully armed fighter, to make diving head-on attack, expending ammunition in single pass, breaking off and landing on skid. Virtually invisible until guns started firing. Conceived 1941, ignored until 1944. Performed well on test but discontinued late 1944. Span 26 ft. (7·9 m.); AuW 2,094 lb. (1,318 kg.); maximum diving speed 292 m.p.h. (467 km./h.).

Captions for Natter: (1) Simplified spruce/ply structure. (2) Spring-loaded parachute container. (3) Fuselage breaking point. (4) Walter HWK 509A motor. (5) T-stoff (hydrogen peroxide oxyquinoline) fuel tank. (6) 20 mm. thick armoured hood. (7) 120 mm. armoured windscreen. (8) Bienenwabe rocket tubes. (9) 24 × 73 mm. Henschel 'Fohn' rockets. (10) Plexiglas nose cone. (11) Control pushrod. (12) C-stoff (hydrazine hydrate methanol water) fuel tank. (13) Stiffening plate to engage launching rail. (14) Laminated ply mainspar. (15) Schmidding solid-fuel boosters (discarded after launch). (16) Combustion chamber. (17) Exhaust nozzle. (18) Elevons.

Captions for BV 40: (1) Triangular fuselage structure, ply/spruce, 4 mm. ply skin. (2) Pitot head. (3) Two 30 mm. Mk 108 cannon in root fairings. (4) 8 mm. sheet metal centre section. (5) Extensible flaps. (6) 12 mm. armoured hood. (7) Gun port. (8) 120 mm. armoured windscreen. (9) Compass housing, 20 mm. frontal armour. (10) Towline and intercom. (11) Landing skid. (12) Detachable launching dolly. (13) Prone pilot. (14) Spruce/ply box spar. (15) Ammunition hatch and conveyor (35 rounds per wing). (16) Aileron pushrod. (17) Wingtip guard. (18) Aileron.

Below, upper: The 1942 experimental DFS glider Klemm 35 composite, leading on to the notorious Mistel Ju88 + Me 109/FW 190 flying-bomb composites of 1944–45.

Centre: Heinkel 162A-2 Volksjager—the 'people's fighter', designed and built in 69 days, first flight December 1944. Remarkably clean design, one piece wooden wing, duralumin monocoque fuselage, plywood nose. Two 30 mm. cannon in cockpit floor. 116 completed, some in service March 1945, but not encountered in action.

Left: Messerschmitt Me 163B Komet; most famous of the 'target defence' fighters, conceived by Alexander Lippisch for DFS in 1941, in service August 1944. Wooden wing, 8 mm. laminated skin, box section spar. Duralumin fuselage shell, built as two halves. Two 30 mm. cannon in wing roots. Undercarriage jettisoned at take off, landing on skid. Nearly 400 built, more lost in accidents than combat.

DH 88 Comet; designed for 1934 England–Australia dash, won by G-ACSS 'Grosvenor House', now to be rebuilt to flying condition. Fuselage of spruce frame, housing 260 gal. (1,173 l.) of fuel in three tanks, two crew in tandem enclosed cockpit. Stressed ply skin, pinned and glued. Wing attached at four points, with laminated fillets.

Foot: DH 91 Albatross; last major wooden airliner, to Imperial Airways requirements, seven delivered from 1937. Fuselage of cedar laminations, 1·5 mm. (inner) and 2·0 mm. (outer) thick, with 22 mm. balsa core, built as one unit over collapsible jig. A most elegant and advanced design, but its teething troubles were never resolved, due to the war.

Right: DH 98 Mosquito; initially to Air Ministry specification B.1/40, March 1940, first flight November 1940, squadron service July 1941. By November 1950, 7,781 built to 41 marks. Construction widely sub-contracted to cabinet-makers etc., even in London's blitz zone, also in Canada and Australia. (See pp. 4–7 for construction.) Shown is Mk. XVIII, with six-pounder shell-gun for anti-shipping strikes.

Wooden aircraft of strategic importance left the stage with a fittingly dramatic flourish: De Havilland's Mosquito, most versatile warplane of World War II; Hornet, fastest prop-driven aeroplane; Swallow, herald of the supersonic age; and Hughes's Hercules, largest aeroplane ever.

Sandwich construction was the kingpin of De Havilland's success, a philosophy of strength through bulk, the grafting together of materials of quite distinct properties for optimum strength and minimum weight. It was the nearest approach to a true monocoque, the skin being sufficiently rigid to warrant only light internal framework. The De Havilland sandwich, as applied to the Albatross, Mosquito, Hornet and parts of the Vampire and Swallow, was ply/balsa/ply, built up over a mould and bonded with Redux synthetic cement. Complete bonding was ensured by securing the shell to its jig with steel straps. Once assembled the fuselage was covered with 'Nadapolam' fabric,

Below centre: DH 103 Hornet; single place long-range fighter, to Air Ministry specification F12/43. First flight July 1944. Too late for war, but served with R.A.F./F.A.A. to late fifties. Fuselage construction as Mosquito; wing with extruded alloy/spruce/compressed ply spars and ribs, Redux bonded. Lower skin of Alclad (aluminium/duralumin), with dural stringers.

Below: DH 100 Vampire, DH's first jet retained the wooden sandwich for the forward fuselage only. The experimental DH 108 Swallow (lower) had Vampire fuselage with laminated wooden wing. Second 108 broke up at Mach 0·9 after failure of mainspar, killing Geoffrey de Havilland jnr. (September 1946). Third 108, with new metal wing, exceeded Mach 1 September 1948, the first pure jet to do so.

thoroughly doped and sanded down to ensure a smooth finish and ideal weather resistance (see also pages 4–7). The De Havilland wing, first used on the DH 88 Comet, was a one-piece two-spar torsion box, with a spruce ply skin of diagonally laid strips, the upper skin of double thickness with stiffening stringers between the plies.

The stresses imposed by supersonic flight cannot be sustained by wooden structures, as demonstrated by the demise of the second DH Swallow. Barring mock-ups and occasional low-speed (or cost) development vehicles, wood no longer figures in the plane-maker's requirements, except in that area of aviation closest akin to the old pioneer era, that of the homebuilder.

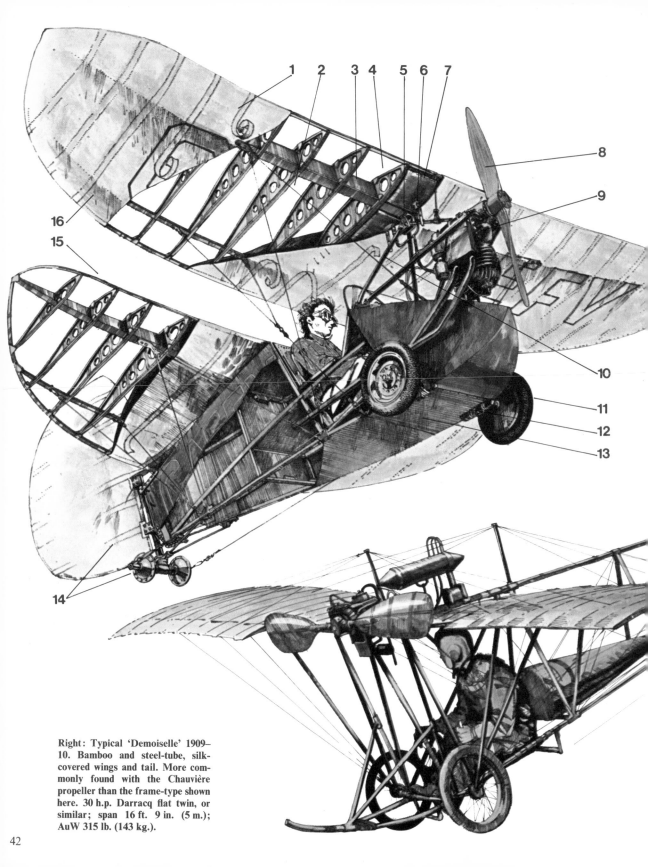

1
2
3
4
5
6
7
8
9
10
11
12
13
14
15
16

Right: Typical 'Demoiselle' 1909–10. Bamboo and steel-tube, silk-covered wings and tail. More commonly found with the Chauvière propeller than the frame-type shown here. 30 h.p. Darracq flat twin, or similar; span 16 ft. 9 in. (5 m.); AuW 315 lb. (143 kg.).

DO-IT-YOURSELF

Left: Mignet HM 14 Pou du Ciel, 1936; considerable development of the basic form was undertaken. Many car and motorcycle engines in the range 20–40 h.p. were acceptable. Span 17 ft. (5 m.)—22 ft. (6.7 m.); AuW 550 lb. (250 kg.); maximum speed, HM 14—60 m.p.h. (96 km./h.), HM 18—100 m.p.h. (160 km./h.).

Captions: (1) Doped linen fabric, laced to ribs. (2) Bracing cables. (3) Box spar; spruce flanges, ply webs. (4) Lightened ply ribs, spruce flanges. (5) Wing pivot. (6) Glass fuel gauges. (7) Brass fuel tank. (8) Beech or walnut propeller cut from a single piece of wood. (9) 25 h.p. Scott Flying-Squirrel; converted motorcycle engine. (10) Steel-tube (bicycle frame) support. (11) Wheelbarrow wheels with low pressure tyres. (12) Bungee cord spring. (13) 'Packing-case' fuselage—$\frac{3}{4}$ in. (19 mm.) spruce frame, 3 mm. birch ply skin, pinned and glued. (14) Combined tailwheel, rudder action. (15) Fixed rear wing. (16) Variable forward wing, Mignet's 'living wing'.

INTRODUCTION

Although all the pioneer aircraft fell into the do-it-yourself category, it was Santos Dumont's *Demoiselle* series that can truly be said to have launched the home built aeroplane. Demonstrated in 1908, S.D.'s No. 19 created a stir by its simplicity and size. Perfected as Nos. 20, 21 and 22, the Demoiselle was promoted as the aeroplane for everyman. Patents and copyrights were not taken out, and construction plans were published in *Popular Mechanics* and a production line set up with Clement-Bayard, the automobile manufacturer. They built about a dozen—rather less than the thousands advocated by Santos Dumont himself, but a score or more may have been built elsewhere. Pilots weighing more than about 120 lb. (54·5 kg.) found the Demoiselle reluctant to leave the ground, and for this reason, out of those built only a handful ever flew, but nevertheless the inspiration was there.

Following World War I a boom in private flying was promised, and governments sponsored competitions in several countries to encourage design. In the interest of economy automobile industries supplied engines, often leaving much to be desired both in power and reliability. In most cases miniaturised conventional aerodynamic form was used, but in France Henri Mignet concluded that this was unnecessarily complex, and therefore eliminated ailerons and elevators. His design relied on a rudder for directional control, a tilting wing for elevation, upswept wingtips for lateral stability and a tandem biplane form to provide an adequate lifting area. His book, *Le Sport de l'Air,* and his craft—the Pou du Ciel or Flying-Flea, sparked off a tidal wave of enthusiasm. He flew to England in August 1935 and within a year no less than 123 planes had been registered for permits to fly. However, a number of fatal accidents occurred, due to the fore and aft pitching movement of the craft being insufficient to recover from a dive of more than 15°, and the Flea was banned. Mignet corrected this fault in his design, but the stigma took a long time to wear off. Currently, his craft, some of which are four seaters, are flying in France and the U.S.A., while only a solitary example still flies in Britain.

Despite the Flea's demise, Mignet's enthusiasm revolutionised the concept of amateur flying. Since the war the movement has gone from strength to strength, with organising bodies such as the Popular Flying Association (PFA), in Britain, and the Experimental Aircraft Association (EAA) in America, co-ordinating design and construction. Wood and steel tube construction are still widely used in amateur aircraft building but are being pressed by the introduction of light alloy and plastic forms such as the Bede BD-5, an American all-aluminium 200 m.p.h. (320 km./h.) craft powered by a 40 h.p. engine. Designed for home construction, it is currently stirring up as much controversy as the Flea did forty years ago.

A

B

C

F

E

G-E

G-EBLV

D

G-ACTD

G-ACT

G-EBHZ

G-

FGH

G

(A) Miles Hawk Major 1936. Wood and fabric. (B) Comper Swift 1930. Wood and fabric. Prized racer. (C) Hawker Cygnet, failed entrant to 1923 Lympne trial. Preserved. Wood and fabric. (D) DH 53 Hummingbird, also failed 1923 trial. 14 built in all. Wood and fabric. (E) DH 60 Moth 1925. Basis of British club flying. Wood and fabric. (F) DH 82 Tiger Moth 1931. Most famous of British sport planes. Wooden wings, steel tube fuselage, fabric covered. (G) Chilton D.W.1a 1937. Miniature racer. Wood and fabric. (H) Percival Mew Gull 1934. Miniature racer—250 m.p.h. (400 km./h.) maximum speed. Wood and fabric. (J) Rollason (Luton) Beta 1966. Popular Formula One racer. Wood and fabric. (K) Luton Minor. Pre-war ultralight inspired by the Flea. Still very popular with homebuilders. Wood and fabric.

(L) Taylor Monoplane 1965. Single seat sports and racer. Wood and fabric. (M) Currie Wot. Pre-war scale replica of Moth for do-it-yourself construction. Still very popular. Illustration shows a 1960 experimental gas turbine powered version.

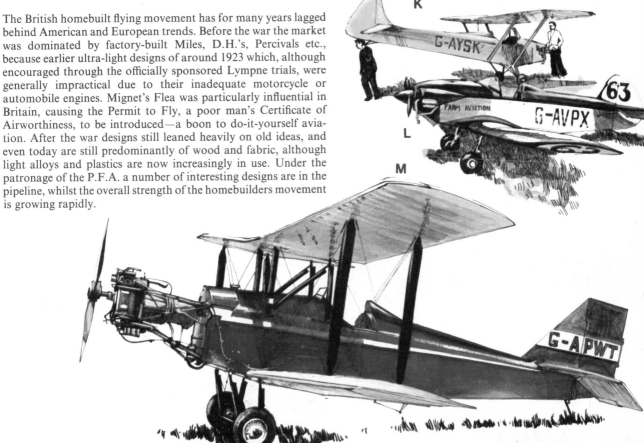

The British homebuilt flying movement has for many years lagged behind American and European trends. Before the war the market was dominated by factory-built Miles, D.H.'s, Percivals etc., because earlier ultra-light designs of around 1923 which, although encouraged through the officially sponsored Lympne trials, were generally impractical due to their inadequate motorcycle or automobile engines. Mignet's Flea was particularly influential in Britain, causing the Permit to Fly, a poor man's Certificate of Airworthiness, to be introduced—a boon to do-it-yourself aviation. After the war designs still leaned heavily on old ideas, and even today are still predominantly of wood and fabric, although light alloys and plastics are now increasingly in use. Under the patronage of the P.F.A. a number of interesting designs are in the pipeline, whilst the overall strength of the homebuilders movement is growing rapidly.

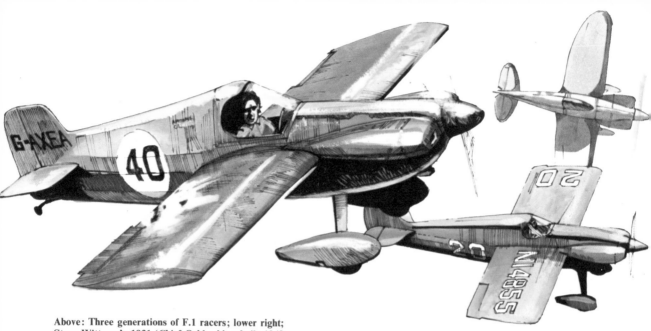

Above: Three generations of F.1 racers; lower right; Steve Wittman's 1931 'Chief Oshkosh', rebuilt 1948 as 'Buster'.

Left: current F.1 favourite—Cassutt Special, type 1 flown 1953. Typical steel-tube/wood/fabric structure. U.K. Airmark-built 111M shown

Top right: Art Williams W-17 Stinger, 1971. All wood, polished ply skin. 223 m.p.h. (357 km./h.) at 1972 Reno races.

Facing page, top: Barney Oldfield's Baby Great Lakes, 1954, scale replica of popular pre-war Great Lakes.

Centre: Best known of U.S. high performance aerobatic biplanes, Pitts Special, Rothmans team S2A two-place shown. S.1 single flown 1947.

American light planes received very little exposure in the European press between the wars. Whilst Mignet reshuffled the basic mores of aerodynamic theory, the American aviation public were able to fly in a wide variety of homebuilt designs in categories not evident elsewhere. Pylon racing, now known as Formula One, with highly powered minimum racers, has long been a popular sport, growing out of the 1920s barnstorming era. The brothers Granville of Gee Bee fame, Benny Howard, Ed Heath, Steve Wittman and many others made their names through such events. Campers and tourers were also widely built, out of which the Pipers, Cessnas and Beechcraft of today developed. In the 1920s the armed forces also took a great interest in ultra-light designs with a view to their use in submarines and on ships, a situation which was repeated in 1972 when the U.S. Navy considered and eventually ordered a homebuilt Pereira Osprey flying boat, as the X-28A, for evaluation for possible use in river liaison in S.E. Asia. The sheer volume and diversity of new lightplane design from America has never diminished, as the annual Oshkosh meet of the E.A.A. never fails to demonstrate.

Left: Homebuilt tourers from the depression era; foreground: Aeronca C-2 (26 h.p. Aeronca); beyond: Pietenpol Aircamper, 1930 (40 h.p. Ford); flying: Heath Parasol, 1929 (various 25–35 h.p.). All with wooden wings, steel tube fuselage, fabric covered.

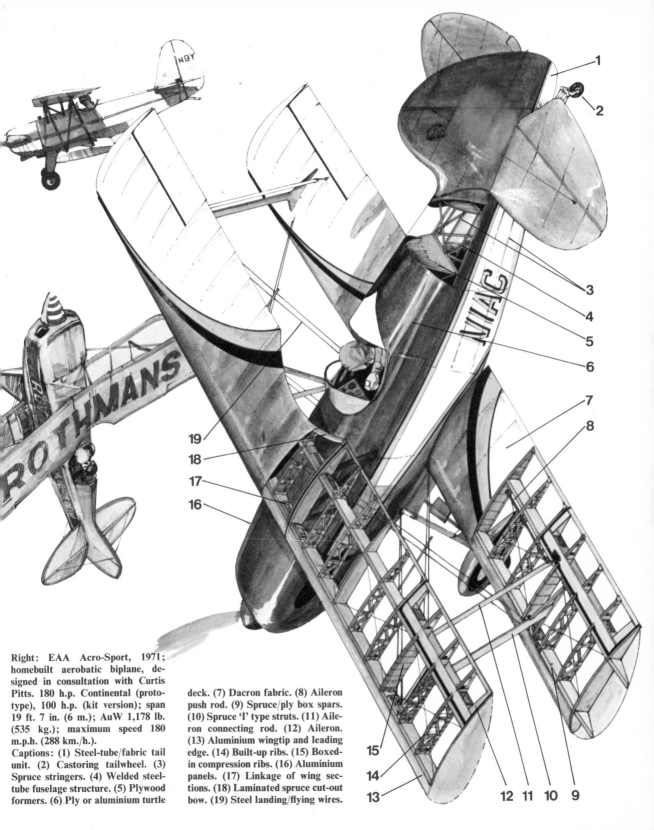

Right: EAA Acro-Sport, 1971; homebuilt aerobatic biplane, designed in consultation with Curtis Pitts. 180 h.p. Continental (prototype), 100 h.p. (kit version); span 19 ft. 7 in. (6 m.); AuW 1,178 lb. (535 kg.); maximum speed 180 m.p.h. (288 km./h.).

Captions: (1) Steel-tube/fabric tail unit. (2) Castoring tailwheel. (3) Spruce stringers. (4) Welded steel-tube fuselage structure. (5) Plywood formers. (6) Ply or aluminium turtle deck. (7) Dacron fabric. (8) Aileron push rod. (9) Spruce/ply box spars. (10) Spruce 'I' type struts. (11) Aileron connecting rod. (12) Aileron. (13) Aluminium wingtip and leading edge. (14) Built-up ribs. (15) Boxed-in compression ribs. (16) Aluminium panels. (17) Linkage of wing sections. (18) Laminated spruce cut-out bow. (19) Steel landing/flying wires.

(A) Ernest Tips's (director of Avions Fairey, Belgium), Tipsy B, 1937; derived from 1935 single-seat type S. Much simplified all wood structure, internal wire bracing replaced with spruce struts to facilitate maintenance. Ply/fabric skin.

(B) Tipsy Nipper, the last Tips design, 1957. Produced in both kit form and as complete aeroplanes. Currently marketed by Nipper Ltd., U.K. Welded steel-tube fuselage, wooden wing, fabric covered.

(C) Jodel D.9 Bebe, 1948. Several hundred, factory, kit or scratch built, still very popular. All wood and fabric. Dihedral wingtips a feature of all Jodels.

European light aviation and sport flying between the wars was linked closely to strong governmental or newspaper support. In Germany, in particular, with its aeroplane industries strictly limited by the constraints of the 1919 Treaty of Versailles, the light plane movement was very strong, and was the breeding ground of important future developments. Through the 1930s club flying was encouraged by the Nazi government for obvious military considerations. Government sponsored competitions in Italy and France prompted public air-mindedness, although minimal designs such as those advocated by Mignet were not encouraged, the widespread appeal of the Flea being attributable to

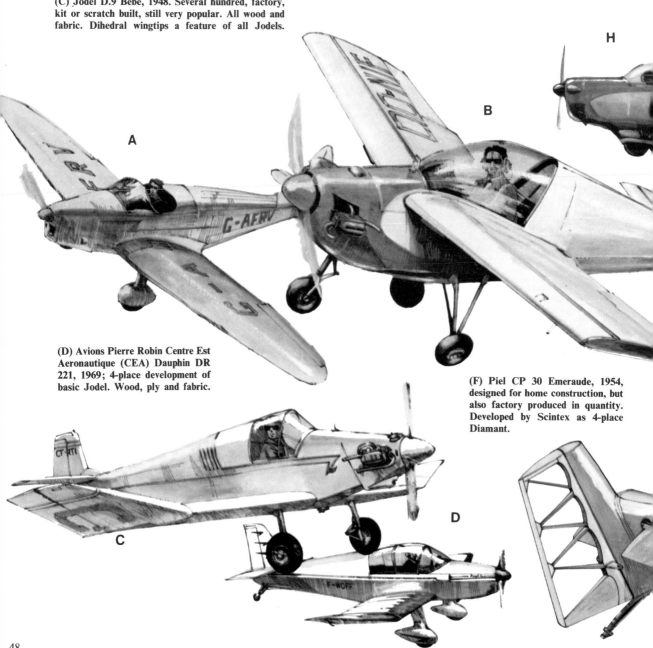

(D) Avions Pierre Robin Centre Est Aeronautique (CEA) Dauphin DR 221, 1969; 4-place development of basic Jodel. Wood, ply and fabric.

(F) Piel CP 30 Emeraude, 1954, designed for home construction, but also factory produced in quantity. Developed by Scintex as 4-place Diamant.

open and occasionally over-enthusiastic, Press support. After World War II, through the inspiration of Joly and Delemontez (Jodel), Druine, Piel, Tips and many others, the growth of home-building has been particularly strong. Volkswagen powerplants, abandoned Wermacht examples of which were first used by Jodel, have remained the fulcrum around which all such do-it-yourself types developed. A handful of manufacturers also manage to compete successfully in an otherwise all-metal United States dominated market, with factory-produced wood-and-fabric aeroplanes.

(H) Powered sailplanes have achieved a new popularity in recent years. The U.S.A.F. adopted the Lockheed Q-Star for silent surveillance in Vietnam, whilst Jim Bede has projected a non-stop round the world flight in a powered Schweitzer glider, as the BD-2 Love, since 1967, currently holding a dis-

tance record for the type at 8,854 miles (14,248 km.). For those of lesser ambition the all-wood French Fournier Avion-Planeur is increasingly popular, likewise the German Scheibe Motorfalke (H).

(E) Roger Druine's D.3 Turbulent, introduced 1950. Very popular throughout Europe, kits produced by Rollason in U.K. French examples with stringer/fabric turtledeck, U.K. with formed ply. Also 2-place tandem D.5 Turbi, side-by-side D.6 Condor. Turbulent: 25–55 h.p. Ardem VW; span 21 ft. 7 in. (6·6 m.); AuW 700 lb. (317 kg.); maximum speed 110 m.p.h. (177 km./h.).

Captions: (1) Fuel tank. (2) Ardem 1,600 c.c. 4-cylinder VW conversion. (3) Slot to maintain control near stall. (4) 3 mm. ply leading edge. (5) Spruce girder ribs. (6) Aileron, duplicates wing structure. (7) Aileron control pulley. (8) Doped fabric, laced to ribs. (9) Light-luggage box. (10) Rudder/elevator control lines. (11) Glued joints with ply 'biscuits'. (12) Ply turtle-deck. (13) Steel tube cockpit frame/turnover bar.

(G) Klemm L.25, 1927, popular German light plane, built also by British Klemm (B. A. Swallow) and Aeromarine in the U.S.

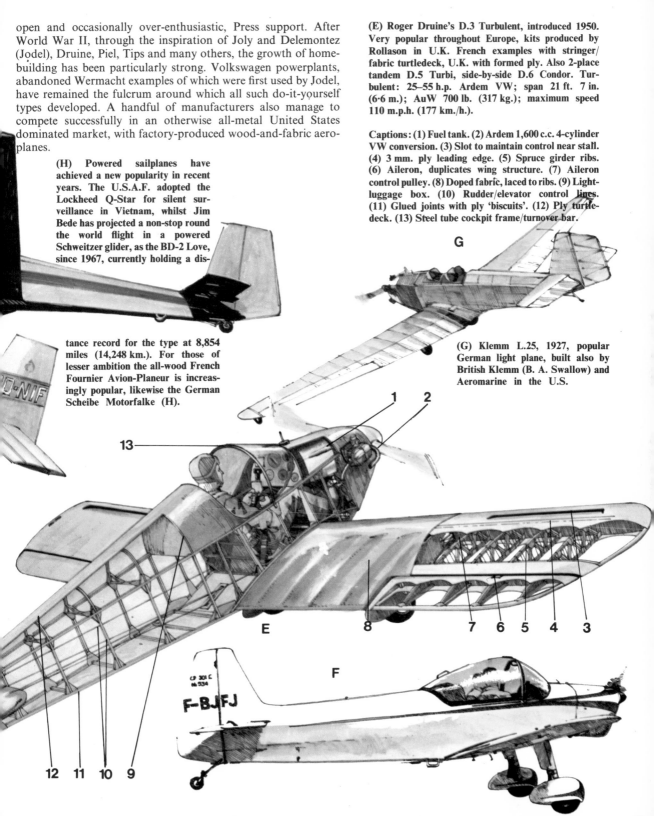

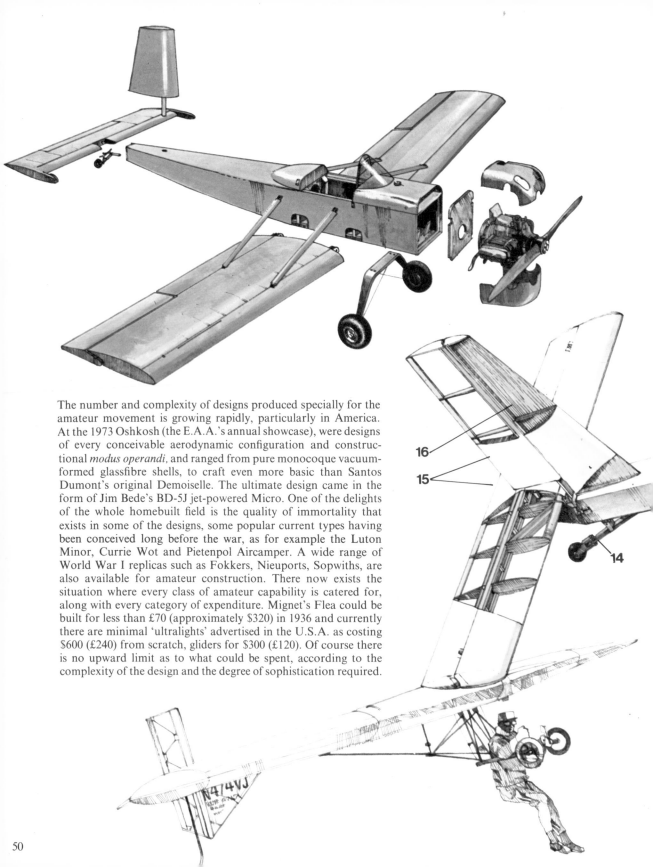

The number and complexity of designs produced specially for the amateur movement is growing rapidly, particularly in America. At the 1973 Oshkosh (the E.A.A.'s annual showcase), were designs of every conceivable aerodynamic configuration and constructional *modus operandi,* and ranged from pure monocoque vacuum-formed glassfibre shells, to craft even more basic than Santos Dumont's original Demoiselle. The ultimate design came in the form of Jim Bede's BD-5J jet-powered Micro. One of the delights of the whole homebuilt field is the quality of immortality that exists in some of the designs, some popular current types having been conceived long before the war, as for example the Luton Minor, Currie Wot and Pietenpol Aircamper. A wide range of World War I replicas such as Fokkers, Nieuports, Sopwiths, are also available for amateur construction. There now exists the situation where every class of amateur capability is catered for, along with every category of expenditure. Mignet's Flea could be built for less than £70 (approximately $320) in 1936 and currently there are minimal 'ultralights' advertised in the U.S.A. as costing $600 (£240) from scratch, gliders for $300 (£120). Of course there is no upward limit as to what could be spent, according to the complexity of the design and the degree of sophistication required.

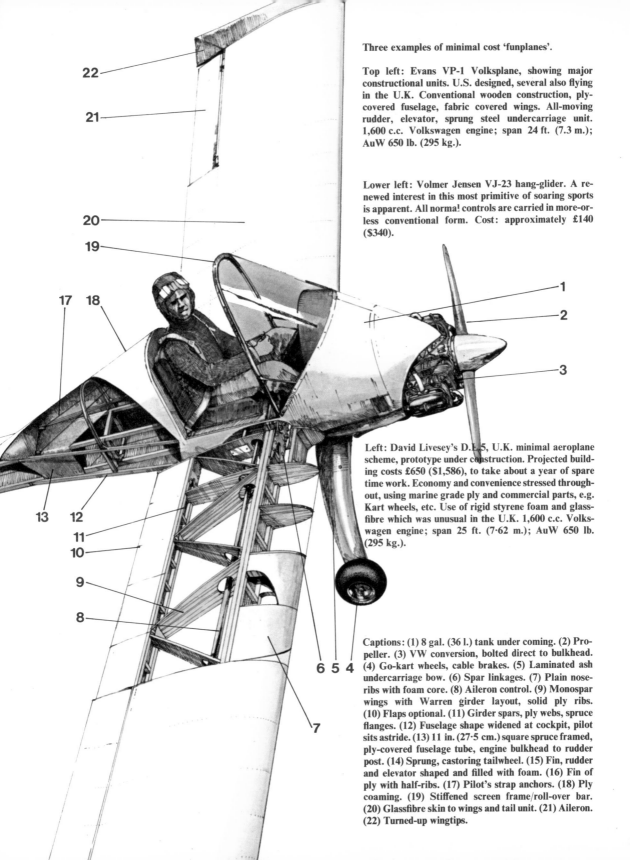

22

21

20

19

17 18

13 12

11

10

9

8

6 5 4

7

1

2

3

Three examples of minimal cost 'funplanes'.

Top left: Evans VP-1 Volksplane, showing major constructional units. U.S. designed, several also flying in the U.K. Conventional wooden construction, ply-covered fuselage, fabric covered wings. All-moving rudder, elevator, sprung steel undercarriage unit. 1,600 c.c. Volkswagen engine; span 24 ft. (7.3 m.); AuW 650 lb. (295 kg.).

Lower left: Volmer Jensen VJ-23 hang-glider. A renewed interest in this most primitive of soaring sports is apparent. All normal controls are carried in more-or-less conventional form. Cost: approximately £140 ($340).

Left: David Livesey's D.L.5, U.K. minimal aeroplane scheme, prototype under construction. Projected building costs £650 ($1,586), to take about a year of spare time work. Economy and convenience stressed throughout, using marine grade ply and commercial parts, e.g. Kart wheels, etc. Use of rigid styrene foam and glass-fibre which was unusual in the U.K. 1,600 c.c. Volkswagen engine; span 25 ft. (7·62 m.); AuW 650 lb. (295 kg.).

Captions: (1) 8 gal. (36 l.) tank under coming. (2) Propeller. (3) VW conversion, bolted direct to bulkhead. (4) Go-kart wheels, cable brakes. (5) Laminated ash undercarriage bow. (6) Spar linkages. (7) Plain nose-ribs with foam core. (8) Aileron control. (9) Monospar wings with Warren girder layout, solid ply ribs. (10) Flaps optional. (11) Girder spars, ply webs, spruce flanges. (12) Fuselage shape widened at cockpit, pilot sits astride. (13) 11 in. (27·5 cm.) square spruce framed, ply-covered fuselage tube, engine bulkhead to rudder post. (14) Sprung, castoring tailwheel. (15) Fin, rudder and elevator shaped and filled with foam. (16) Fin of ply with half-ribs. (17) Pilot's strap anchors. (18) Ply coaming. (19) Stiffened screen frame/roll-over bar. (20) Glassfibre skin to wings and tail unit. (21) Aileron. (22) Turned-up wingtips.

INDEX

Below: Dr. Alexander Graham Bell's Cygnet, 1907, representing one of the many novel approaches to the problem of flight from the first decade of this century. In this case the lifting surface was of many tetrahedral cells, each of which was intended to be a self-contained aerodynamic unit. It was flown successfully as a towed kite, with Lieut. Selfridge of the A.E.A. on board, but was far too structurally cumbersome to be of any practical value. The Cygnet is shown on its lighter (as a kite it was towed behind a ship), with Selfridge laying amidships and Bell standing on the quay.

(1) Sitka spruce *(Picea sitchensis)*: northern temperate conifer rising to 200–300 ft. 23–32 lb. per cu. ft. Principally from N. America. Light yellow-brown, straight grain, uniform texture. Most extensively cultivated of commercial timbers, all domestic purposes, mainly for paper pulp. All primary structures in aircraft. Low resistance to specific pests and fungi.

(2) Douglas Fir *(Pseudotsuga taxifolia)*: similar environs to Sitka, rising to 150–250 ft. 32–42 lb. per cu. ft. Orange-brown, straight grain, uneven texture. Similar properties to Sitka, but heavier, also lack of resistance to pests.

(3) Ash *(Fraxinus excelsior)*: temperate hardwood, 80–150 ft. 40–53 lb. per cu. ft. Europe and U.S.A. Light yellow-brown, straight grain, uneven texture. One time principal aircraft wood in Europe. Excellent shock/compression resistance.

1

2

3